PAUL TOURNIER'S
MEDICINE
OF THE
WHOLE PERSON

PAUL TOURNIER'S
MEDICINE
OF THE
WHOLE PERSON

39 essays
honoring the founder of
a school of medical practice
dedicated to treating each patient
as a human being

WORD BOOKS, PUBLISHER, WACO, TEXAS

PAUL TOURNIER'S
MEDICINE OF THE WHOLE PERSON

First Printing—April 1973
Second Printing—August 1973

Copyright © 1973 by Word, Incorporated
Waco, Texas 76703

Library of Congress catalog card number: 73-76259
Printed in the United States of America

*Lovingly dedicated
to Paul Tournier
on the occasion of his
seventy-fifth birthday*

Contents

Foreword

In 1940, Dr. Paul Tournier, internist from Geneva, Switzerland, published his first book, with the French title *Médecine de la Personne*, which in English means medicine of the whole person. He wanted to express the idea that neither classical medicine, based on the knowledge of natural science, nor psychosomatic medicine, based on the experience of deep psychology brought forth by Sigmund Freud, Carl Gustav Jung, and others, covered all healing potentialities. The medicine taught at medical and psychological schools considered the sick person in an objective way, whereas Dr. Tournier, dissatisfied with this view, had a vision of the mystery of persons, which cannot be revealed by objective methods of science.

Influenced by the philosophy of Martin Buber, and after many conversations with medical friends of the Oxford group, founded by Frank Buchman, Dr. Tournier decided to invite, together with his friends Dr. Jean de Rougemont of Lyon, France, and Dr. Alphonse Maeder of Zürich, Switzerland, medical doctors of all specialties and all countries to a first retreat on "the medicine of the whole person" in order to study the problems posed by the vision of the mystery of the person. Buber suggested that there are two ways of approaching people; one in which we consider people as objects; the other in which we consider people as subjects. The first relationships can be expressed by "I-it", the second by "I-you".

The first study-week took place August 24–31, 1947, at the Ecumenical Institute of Bossey, Switzerland. Since then, every year in the summertime one study-week has taken place in different European countries, visited by about one hundred medical doctors from different countries, forming a group known as the medical group of Bossey or medical group of *Médecine de la personne*.

The conferences of this group are different from all medical conferences of scientific character. They are based on the prin-

*Bossey, meeting place for
medicine of the whole person*

*The Bossey medical group
at Novara, Italy, 1968*

ciple that the medicine of the whole person begins with the person of the doctor himself. Therefore, at the conferences, personal talks form the core of the day, and in the evenings different participants and their marital partners share personal experiences with the whole group.

As far as the objective aspect of the medicine of the whole person is concerned, the conferences tried to find ways and methods to show that such a medicine is in practice. Many results came out of the experiences of the participants and the group itself.

To help a patient in the understanding of a whole life, his existence in his environment and his biography—objects of classical medicine, comprising psychology and social aspects—are absolutely necessary. But, moreover, he should find an understanding of himself as a person. To do so requires no more analysis, but rather a personal approach by the doctor—no matter of what discipline of medicine—expressed by a personal dialogue, by a loving attitude, by prayer, by compassion, by sharing personal experiences, by mutual and yet common quietness, etc. Religiously speaking, the patient is in the light of God, insofar as the doctor of medicine looks upon him as a person. To put it in another way, the doctor of the person will look through all the façades or identities of his patient to sense in a mystical way the uniqueness of the person.

No specific Christian doctrine is the basis of the medicine of the whole person: any doctor who is ready to consider himself and the patient as a unique person might practice a medicine of the whole person. However, the Bible seems to be the most adequate basis for a guideline to its meaning. The group of doctors of the medicine of the whole person, comprising mainly Christians of all denominations, does not practice proselytism and does not exclude non-Christians. The study-weeks have been inspired by morning Bible studies, presented in a masterful way by Dr. Tournier himself, and later on, by other members of the group. Many books written by Dr. Tournier were the result of those Bible studies and the conferences.

Two offspring of the Bossey medical group are now active in the United States—one in Louisville, Kentucky, and the other, an interstate group formed in the fall of 1972, with headquarters in North Carolina. Open to ministers and social workers as well as medical men, they are called "Medicine and Ministry of the Whole Person."

The group has stated many other objectives of a medicine of the whole person: to help patients find the meaning of their sickness and their life; to deal with the problem of death; to discover a specific ethical approach to their environment; to open sources of love for themselves and for their fellow-men; to sense the meaning of suffering as a sacrifice in the understanding of Christ; to find strength through the community for a new responsibility towards themselves and their fellow-men. Dr. Tournier would never agree with a definition of the person; therefore there is no definition of the medicine of the person. On the other hand, the notion of medicine of the person can be applied to other disciplines: one can be a lawyer of the person, businessman of the person, interpreter of the person, teacher of the person, social worker of the person, etc. This jubilee book, intended as homage for the great lover of people, Dr. Paul Tournier, presents ideas and experiences of many friends of his who have benefited from his books, his weeks of studies and, last but not least—from his person himself and the person of his companion of life and work, Nelly Tournier.

BERNARD HARNIK

Zürich, Switzerland
December, 1972

JEAN DE ROUGEMONT, M.D.

Professor, Surgeon
Lyon, France

The Vocation of Paul Tournier

My dear Paul,

You used to like to chat by your fireside with those who needed your help.

Today, the armchair reserved for your companions is occupied by an old friend. From the store of shared memories, which you will forgive my skipping, I am going to try to talk about the vocation which led you to practice medicine in a very special way.

Your desire to serve others dates from a long time ago when, fresh out of prep school, with a career to decide upon, several possibilities offered themselves. The bar did not interest you. The example of your father and your faith might have led you to the church. Instead you chose medicine.

When you opened your private office, the name plate indicated no specialty. Instead it carried the one word: Internist. Under this sign you began your dealings with the sick.

Though you, like any capable and conscientious physician, examined, formulated a diagnosis, and prescribed treatment, the mental role of the patient interested you extremely. You must have observed that many men and women were in trouble with themselves and consequently with those around them and society in general. These intimate problems you very felicitously called "life problems." Your major objective was revealing itself. Your

15

obvious solicitude for people in pain aroused their need to pour
out their troubles to someone.

For, especially in modern society, silence and solitude op-
press those who cannot or will not unburden themselves, perhaps after an unfortunate first attempt, to a member of the family
or even a professional counselor.

Well, in your case, they finally had found someone who would
listen and try to understand without judging. Feeling your re-
ceptivity, close yet impersonal, the timid expressed their feelings
and the distrustful let themselves go. Suddenly, or bit by bit,
you gathered their secrets, hard to carry within, hard to receive.

So patients poured in, both because of your professional rep-
utation and because the unique quality of your reception of
them became known through word of mouth. As for you, you
learned what results can be obtained from a totally dedicated
doctor.

However, this method of double practice brought about a very
profound change within yourself, and you began to recognize
that you were more interested in life problems than in organic
pathology.

Excited by the adventure, as you might say it yourself, you
were tempted to leave the beaten path and to depart on an ex-
ploration of the "realm of the soul." Shaken up, still hesitant, you
must have reflected a long time and weighed the pros and cons.
Indeed, the enterprise embodied some risk. You had a family,
a wife and two sons, and you could not without some apprehension carry them with you toward some new and possibly hazardous destiny.

But on a certain day and in a certain spot in the country around
Geneva (you later gave me the exact details) you vowed to
dedicate yourself to people overwhelmed by their life problems.
You were obeying an order discerned through faith. Liberated,
you were able to understand more clearly the spiritual meaning
of your vocation.

Your wife, Nelly, who had shared in the debate, approved the
decision of a husband whom she firmly upheld in all things.

Doctor Tournier could now let it be known that henceforth he
would work exclusively with patients who were ready to bring
to him their mental problems.

What followed proved you had been right. Little by little

there appeared on your engagement calendar the names of these new patients—sick, though they were outwardly well. Sometimes, though, you would suspect that behind their life problems lurked a physical disorder. At those times, you would examine the patient and send him back to his regular physician. Similarly, you would know how to uncover the cases who needed a psychiatrist or an analyst and refer them to colleagues.

But plenty were left to engage your efforts and your time. Boys and girls crushed by strict parental authority or the prey of a possessive mother, children deteriorating under the lack of affection and family discord, adolescents in crisis, troubled couples, bachelors not yet resigned to their state, abandoned old people—so many victims of the painful human relationship. And also so many factors of present or future misunderstanding.

Except for dispensing with drugs, what value was there for these souls, slightly or seriously crippled, in the attentive listening, the solicitous words of comfort? Some went away quickly, comforted, knowing they could return; others needed to be followed week by week, for months on end, before they tried to make it alone. Some fell, and once again you took them in charge. Yet others were not able to do without you and came back periodically to be encouraged. Most feared even more than death the problems of life. And for thirty years, risking your own well-being, you cared for them, the gravely ill as well as the slightly ill.

But your activities did not stop with this exhausting therapy. You were gathering copious clinical documentation, which resulted in your publishing a long series of works. Translated into several languages, they had two major consequences: invitations to lecture in several countries and an exchange of correspondence with physicians of ten nationalities.

At Celigny, you brought together for the first time a certain number of these people. It was the beginning of the Bossey group, the history of which has been written by Armand Vincent. In spite of yourself, you became founder of a school! In 1968, you called together the board of directors to pass responsibilities along to the younger colleagues. You had in mind to retire from practice and live in your house at Troinex.

As you well know, Paul, the medicine of the whole person as

practiced by you produces serious doubts in those colleagues who have not had the privilege of knowing you. Some esteem that the rhythm of modern life and the growing exigencies of technology do not leave them enough time to care for the mental aspect of the person. For others, your therapy is founded on membership in a church; they state they cannot countenance a "religious medicine." Still others deny a method which involves emotional obligation, good perhaps in pediatrics, but dangerous in dealing with fully developed individuals and especially questionable in dealing with girls and women.

By your conduct, Paul, you demonstrated that emotional involvement simply means goodness. Goodness is expressed in the intonations of a voice, and in silence through the attitude, the gesture, the face, the expression. Technique helps the body. Goodness permits the physician wrapped up in his profession to bring help to the troubled mind, to which he may bring peace and comfort. This very efficacious action goes hand in hand with greater availability to the patient.

When a psychiatrist or an analyst displays goodness, even if he doesn't agree to this, he outclasses the good specialist in his field. Reason approves goodness but never orders it. Goodness owes nothing to the physical makeup, the temperament or the character. It is a function to which there is but one obstacle: you defined it—life problems.

The spring which feeds goodness, you pointed it out; the relationship to this spring, you explained it; whence from that time you employed a special language. Yours, they say, is religious. I would say, more exactly, a dynamic faith, inspired by a lived experience. Here one divines the secret of yourself. You have been accorded that pardon that most men do not accept and that no man could accord himself, that liberating new start which loosens the bonds of a paralyzing and sterile guilt.

From that time, you could, far from proposing yourself as healer, promise your patients that a cripple can walk if he will let himself be cared for by the Great Physician, who alone can awaken in the heart of each of us healing spiritual strength. Did you not sometimes even confide in a patient one of your own life problems?

In many ways your language was new to many of your believing patients. Because of your obvious tolerance, it did not offend those who were declared agnostics or atheists. All of them felt comforted and your enthusiasm moved them.

Should one deduce from this brief biography that one may become physician of the whole person simply by imitating you in all things? You have always vigorously denied this. To conclude, an example will illustrate your attitude.

When two physicians with opposite spiritual convictions show their patients an equal and persevering goodness, both realize the inner difficulties to be surmounted before this service can be performed. Both know that the will does not suffice. Aragon would say: the first believes in heaven and the second does not. The first believes and thinks he has found there the origin of healing power and so states. The second can scarcely believe in an origin which he finds uncertain. He employs less explicit terms in speaking of it. *Words*—there is the ultimate difference between them. In fact, what will count are *acts* devoted to the whole person.

Which you, dear Paul, have amply proclaimed and proved.

ROBERT D. BONE, M.D.

Internal Medicine
Corsicana, Texas

My Encounter with Paul Tournier

A missionary home on furlough once told me that people tend to put Paul Tournier in one of three categories. Some think he has achieved the ultimate in human values. Some think he has discarded all reasonable sanity and has lost the possibility of real achievement. Others think that he, as a missionary, has no relevance to this century and its people. My friend rejects each of these judgments, for "I think that I am nothing other than a man who knows his job and has found his place . . . and it should be the same for any man, whether barber, lawyer, or clerk."

Paul Tournier has made a great impression on me as a sensitive man who has discovered, accepted, and revealed his true self and has found his place in the scheme of things. The dual fulfillment of knowing one's self and finding one's place realizes its greatest value when it is used to help someone else make the same discovery. When Paul Tournier told about his life, I felt as if he had seen and was telling parts from my own life, for I too had wrestled with the dilemma of a three-way split in vocation among medicine, psychology, and theology.

The place of encounter was Laity Lodge in the remote hill country of Southwest Texas. The time was Paul Tournier's latest visit to the United States in 1964. The group was small and made up of ministers, doctors, professors, and psychologists. Receiving an invitation to join this select group was an honor for me, and the appeal of the invitation was strengthened by my knowledge that Dr. Tournier was a physician interested in the whole person.

The location of the meeting had a very special attraction. Twenty years before it became Laity Lodge, I had been there on summer vacations with my young wife. Then it was a remote, rocky river canyon in the undeveloped "wide open spaces." We had "explored" the river on foot on all-day hikes and on campouts. The water is cold and crystal clear, wonderful for a swim in the deeper places. The river bed and overhanging cliffs are rugged limestone; the soil is rocky and barren. The inviting hills are covered with knotted cedar trees that give an aroma of freshness to the air. The sky is ever clean, and the stars are clear and brilliant at night. On our summer vacations to the Frio River Canyon all the problems of the world seemed very distant, and God seemed so near. It was there that I dreamed of becoming a doctor of medicine worthy of the name. Year after year it was a place of inspiration and renewed conviction.

From my first meeting with Dr. Tournier I heard him say something I wanted to believe but had never heard anyone say so succinctly as he: that the practice of my specialty of internal medicine is compatible with the strong dual interest of psychology and psychotherapy. He stated clearly that these two merge with acknowledging in reverence the Creator of life in dealing with the problems of pain, suffering, and death. It was as though he spoke to me individually, "Yes, the field of internal medicine is definitely related to the unseen area of human feelings that drive men in mysterious ways, and beyond that, reverence for life and response to God are interrelated to caring for patients."

In my years of training for internal medicine, only one professor had spoken of the internist becoming seriously involved with the patients' emotional problems, and that man had undergone psychoanalysis after entering into practice. He said that his personal gratification from being able to diagnose symptoms "made the analysis worthwhile," and that his ability to understand symptoms jumped from around 60 to over 90 percent.

The dilemma came to me in much the same way as to Dr. Tournier. How does the internist excuse himself for not remaining devoted to the exploding library of medical knowledge while spending fairly large segments of time in psychotherapy (for which he has not been formally trained)? It was reassuring to hear Dr. Tournier say that the most helpful—indeed, perhaps the only available—ear to hear the patient may be the non-psychiatrist doctor who practices medicine of the whole person.

This was true of a young engineer-executive who came to me complaining of chest pain and difficulty in breathing. All of the studies made on him were normal; he was in fact the best physical specimen I had seen in months. He was perfectly disciplined in diet and exercise, yet he was seized by an illogical incapacitating fear. He told me of his father, who "died when he was the age I am now." The man was everything a boy could wish of a father, and the patient's fondest memory of boyhood was the almost constant companionship of dad and son. "But he took no care of himself. He had emphysema and smoked too much. . . . He had chest pain and difficulty in breathing, and he died of pneumonia." Once the patient's fear of death had found freedom of expression, the symptoms of disability began to fade away. I understood the man well and was able to tell him about similar fears of my own, even the fear of growing to mature manhood. I feared growing up like my father, who was struck down by tuberculosis. In my case, fear seemed to work as a psychological deterrent to achieving—to growing up and becoming vulnerable, in contrast to remaining small and safe.

Medicine of the whole person invariably leads one into a spiritual dimension. Perhaps it is here that I have received the greatest benefit from Paul Tournier. First, he had translated the Christian faith for me into a way of life which I can share with my patients and colleagues. It is not necessary to become a pastor or a priest to effectively share our own feeling and knowledge of God. Secondly, it has been very helpful for me to see the way Paul Tournier accepts the religious experiences of other persons as uniquely their own; he apparently feels no necessity to "correct" their experiences and make them conform to his ideas. It speaks of deep spiritual perception to hear a Protestant physician recommend that the Catholic patient return to his priest for a specific malady of the wounded soul which has made the body ill. The third benefit has come from the humility with which Dr. Tournier shares his theology. Great knowledge or experience is sometimes overpowering and may be made to seem out of reach, yet his translation of biblical lessons into the daily experiences of our human situation has the opposite effect. He shows that the personal experience of faith is easily within our reach. There is a certain deepening of the relationship between doctor and patient when a spiritual dialogue has occurred. Medicine of the person seems neither to probe this area aggressively nor to avoid the occasion to listen or to speak. How often does the physician hear the request for prayer in the confrontation with pain, separation from a loved one, or death?

Not the least of my gratitude to Dr. Paul Tournier is for the growing reward of gaining so many new physician friends from other countries. In this age of specialization, there are many pressures which channel the physician into the ever-narrowing road of his particular practice. How much of this world we miss and never know of in our sheltered, restricted, and busy lives. The very nature of the Bossey conferences allows us to come to know one another as individuals with personal feelings, an experience available to no other professional group. Dr. Tournier's books are filled with references to the experiences of other physicians which are related at the annual meeting of *Médecine de la personne*. It is one of my life's treasures to share this experience with all of you, and it is an honor to be asked to write these words in tribute to our esteemed friend.

KAREL ZUIDEMA, M.D.

General Practitioner
Wezep, Holland

Medicine of the Whole Person and the Road Ahead

When I complied with Armand Vincent's request to contribute an article to the present volume I realized that my voice should be a representative one, and comprise every facet of what *médecine de la personne* (the medicine of the whole person) has achieved in my country. This is, however, impossible.

Many people have read Paul Tournier's books, many physicians included. His first book was translated into Dutch, and five times reprinted!

It is well-known that in the fifties many Dutch colleagues attended the conferences of *médecine de la personne*. But what is lacking is even the slightest organizational unity among these physicians, which is typical for Paul Tournier himself. That is why I am not acquainted with any of the Tournier friends in my country, so that I can only speak for myself.

Five years ago I first came into contact with the medicine of the whole person through Jan van der Hoeven, who had supported Paul Tournier's ideas from the very first and had attended the Bossey weeks ever since they began. He is to a certain extent representative of the Dutch Tournier friends, and asked me to replace him at the next meeting. This occurred quite spontaneously, in spite of my difficulty with the language.

This language barrier should certainly not be underrated, for is not this very language barrier a symptom of mankind's illness, originating as it does from the building of the Tower of Babel, which was to be a symbol of man's independence of God? Has this language barrier perhaps something to do with national pride? Was this division into nations, speaking different languages, part of the Creator's original plan? Or can it be that God only allowed this division merely as a second-rate form of terrestrial government to enable Israel to have its earthly kingdom, which it preferred to its God-given theocracy?

In a personal conversation I had with Jan van der Hoeven, he told me: "You should go to the Bossey conference. When you get into contact with these people, and hear their message, it will make an indelible impression on you; you will never be able to disengage yourself from it. Paul has taught me to read my Bible again. It is amazing how this man must have ploughed through his Bible."

I went to the last five conferences, and after much listening, which is difficult for me, and reading a few books by Paul Tournier, I have come to realize that his message is the answer to the rationalistic medical science of our time, a medical science which we have studied, in which we believe, which is taught in universities all over the world, except in China, and practiced everywhere. And, as we should not fail to admit, it is rightly regarded as a great blessing for mankind.

But medical science has dissociated itself from the impulse that caused its birth and developed it, and which is still the force that makes it grow at an enormous rate. That impulse is: sympathy for one's fellow-men. But the gradual waning of this sympathy, this fellow-feeling, has resulted in a kind of fossilization, an impoverishment, which eventually leads to a medical science for its own purpose and glory.

During a medical conference which I attended, a general practitioner like myself said: "We ought not to be so ethical and give ourselves airs. Our profession is essentially not different from the trade of the baker. He distributes his bread as we do our pocket health care, and we are paid very well for it."

Medical science has come to lead a life of its own, detached from philosophy and theology.

The call for a spiritual revival, for renovation, for a return to the ultimate source from which care for our neighbor springs, is the purpose of Paul Tournier's life. His aim is a medical science that intercedes for the human being who is our patient, but just as much our neighbor, our fellow-man.

Of course, psychosomatically minded colleagues are interested in medicine of the person.

Medical science cannot but admit that, in spite of the enormous progress made in the nineteenth and twentieth centuries, there are still many incurable illnesses (Professor Siebeck, Dr. Huebschmann). But there is more. In his book *The Personage and the Person*, Paul Tournier tries to penetrate into the mystery of the "unknown man" (Alexis Carrel), and does not hesitate to have recourse to auxiliary sciences such as psychology and psychoanalysis.

Only by reading all Paul Tournier's books can one get a detailed understanding of how he has been conditioned and how his ideas have developed. From the outset he has been considerably influenced by the Oxford Movement of Frank Buchman.

A number of his books are now out of print. Perhaps it would be possible to form a permanent secretariat, which could undertake to lend out these books, and at the same time serve as an international communication center for Christian medical associations.

Paul Tournier's passionate search for what is the essence of our medical profession has led him to the insight that what is really at the heart of man's illness is his being separated from his Creator, his lost relationship with God.

The discovery and elaboration of this conception of human illness, and the demonstration of the existence of this relation, has attracted many physicians. The great importance of the gospel—the biblical message—for our modern Western secularized medical science has been irrefutably revealed by the productive life of Paul Tournier.

Certainly the environment in which Paul Tournier grew up had a stipulating effect on him, and determined to a certain extent the way in which he performs his medical work.

Let me repeat: modern medical science is the result of all that has been discovered, invented, and elaborated during the past centuries, during which investigators of all disciplines have given their lifetimes to acquire this enormous mass of medical knowledge. Of course we must keep wholly up to date technically, and this takes much of our time. We have to deal with this technical aspect of medical science every day, and we should not fail to be solidly equipped with this medical science. But, and this is the point, medical technology cannot have the last word.

What has the gospel, the message that has been passed on by the churches through the ages, to do with our daily work as physicians?

The beginning of the conferences in Bossey in 1947 as an ecumenical center is an indication of the spirit which propels the medicine of the whole person. Is not the ecumenical movement, which revaluates the unity of the divided churches in accordance with the teachings of their Lord, the result of that same spirit? Should the teachings of the gospel and medical science remain separated, and must physicians and clergymen continue to operate in two clearly distinguished fields of activity? This is, indeed, the general opinion in my country.

It is true that the regular hospital chaplain is an esteemed member of the hospital staff, with his own chair at the staff meetings, his own room and consultation hours—but also with his own clearly defined territory, in which he is expected to approach things from a spiritual point of view, in his function of "spiritual specialist." Preaching the gospel is thus an organized and specialistic affair, and may be resorted to when the patient asks for it. It is simply a separate "item" in our "health packet." And in the same way the aid to underdeveloped countries is separated from the name of Christ, who taught us to help our neighbor. But when we dissociate the material and the spiritual aspects of things they become secularized: they materialize and die.

We are going in the wrong direction if we think that prosperity means happiness and peace for mankind. Satan once tempted our Lord by promising him to give this material prosperity to the whole world. Christ withstood that temptation, but what about us?

The liberation of our patient's spirit is essential for his spiritual health. The protesting youngsters of our days are a symptom of a "deficiency illness." The escape into sexuality and drugs, the popularity of oriental religious experience, and our modern "consumption society" point to a world-wide endemic deficiency of spiritual life, of prayer, of relationship with God, who revealed himself to us in his Son Jesus Christ. Young people believe they can be liberated from our materialistic world, but what really happens is that they become addicted to a modern form of the most pernicious slavery.

Medicine of the whole person starts right at home in our own family, our own marriage, our own heart, our own thoughts. And it involves a personal relationship with our patients, because they are our neighbors. This attitude does not necessarily mean being religious, Catholic or Protestant, but it does mean that we dedicate our personal lives to the personal and living Lord, who stands revealed in our Bible. It means the reestablishment of our relationship with God, the God of Israel, the father of our Lord Jesus Christ.

If the conferences and the minds of the participants remain accessible to this spirit, the impulse to continue and develop, which is necessary for any movement if it is to survive, will endure.

A great many physicians are attracted by the conferences and the works of Paul Tournier. A large-scale dialogue has been launched. But the fire of the spirit must burn on in our own hearts and minds. And through this fire our patient can be healed.

ENSIO KURKIO-SUONIO, M.D.

Gynecologist
Hämeenlinna, Finland

Concerning the Temptations of the Christian Doctor

To be tempted is part of man's existence in this world. Temptation is like a force of gravity which holds us down; which, in the Christian language, is called sin. The New Testament uses for sin the word *hamartia,* a "falling short"; for example, an arrow which does not reach its goal. The richer the life, the greater the possibility of not reaching the complete goal. The profession of doctor is a particularly abundant one, and numerous temptations of a special sort follow him.

As a man, the doctor naturally is tempted by the same temptations as everyone else—in the area of his character defects, his bad habits, and the influence of his environment. Nevertheless, there are still special individual features of the profession. For the doctor who wants to be Christian, temptations mostly take two directions: deviation to the left or to the right.

To the left there lie in ambush the negligence of church morals and of the Christian life-style, merging into this world. The doctor is obligated as no one else to live within call of man, in an attitude *nil humani mihi alienum sit.* Also his work often demands ignoring or interrupting the particular hours dedicated to the church which others can regularly observe. Indeed, his Christian duty often demands that he neglect the worship service in order to complete a pressing operation, or to visit a patient. But how easily we slip off more and more to the left, aloof from the normal rhythm of the rest of the community of Christ.

We begin to feel our alienation as natural, and we forget the regular breath of the air of eternity.

In addition, many a doctor, because of his good education, succumbs easily to the temptation to hold himself at a certain distance from the less educated church people. He makes this impression not only through his absence, but also perhaps through a greater worldliness in word and deed, in his pleasures and amusements. It has an effect when he, the fine educated man, utters a quick swear word. He easily earns the glory of a true doctor both in his own conscience and in the eye of the greater public if he destroys with novel gestures the marks of a trivial and narrow-minded faithfulness, and keeps himself apart from everything which might be termed Pharisaism. Behind that, to be sure, stands a kernel of true insight. But at the same time, there lies in waiting a clearer way to the left, a temptation to separate oneself complacently from the annoying, undeveloped community of the children of God. Certain courage is demanded from the doctor to be as a Christian exactly what he is, without striving for the current highly treasured stamp of a publican and sinner or to crown himself impressively with extraordinary humility.

However, the pull to the right means to us a worse and often much more malignant temptation: the practice of religion can be a masked flight from the difficult troubles to which God has called the doctor. To offer pious words as partial substitute for sufficient examination and trustworthy diagnosis is a swindle to the patient. And to replace anticipated therapy by the doctor with prayer would be blasphemy of God.

The possibilities of a competent diagnosis and therapy presuppose continued learning, unceasing further education. In fact, the Christian faith obligates the doctor to read much that is worldly, to take part in congresses and courses, and to follow closely the development of his worldly specialty. There is actually a temptation to such spirituality which can contribute to sin in the permanently practicing doctor. At this point the shrewd warning of the Bible (Eccles. 7:16) concerning false balance of piety is appropriate: "Be not righteous over much and be not over wise; why should you destroy yourself?" The many warnings in the Old Testament against a religiosity which is disagreeable to God illumine this fact; for example, the oft-repeated prohibition not only of idolatry itself, but also the sacrifice to the one true God, to Yahweh himself, at a self-chosen high place of one's own liking. The Apostle Paul writes similarly concerning the self-choosing spirituality (Col. 2:23).

Such warnings are naturally to be understood rightly. By no means do they justify the removal of the spiritual life either from the doctor himself, or from his patients. Of course, as a Christian, the doctor too prays in the practice of his specialty—as a rule, in secret. However, in the absence of objective—one would like to say, materialistic-scientific—honesty his spirituality is not genuine.

Here a marginal note must be added. During my youth, it was still possible, at least with us in Finland, to set up as an ideal, a perfect doctor, who was master of practically everything professional and always kept himself at the peak of exact capability. There were still several personalities of that type among us in many places in the country. Today it would be unreasonable even to imagine such a possibility, and whoever strives after it follows a *fata morgana*. The Christian faith, however, calls us to no such beautiful fiction, but only to strict reality. The perfect doctor today is no longer a natural man. The Lord wishes from his children no imaginary unnaturalness, no such feature of the personality which when all is said and done—*mirabile dictu*—makes us, in spite of everything, less useful.

The tension between medical perfection and the human-natural possibility is always there for the Christian. The push to an ever further specialization of the doctor which today is evident everywhere in the world originates, in my opinion, in considerable part, from this tension which is causing us permanent torment of conscience and personal discontent. And this again brings new problems to us which I cannot go into in this context. Indeed, nowhere has our Lord promised the doctor in his discipleship a problem-free, splendid life ruled always according to the book. But he has promised to be with us every day. A certain painful and humble feature of imperfection belongs to the perfection of the profession of a Christian doctor. For in the ideal of perfection of the doctor also stands a secret temptation which can lead us to *hamartia*, falling short of the goal.

Strangely, one often sees how the piety which deviates to the right accompanies the propensity to mammon. Actually the same temptation in the same manner also threatens the left. But on the right, this inclination is especially glaring. And here is it also

more easily disguised under the cover of respectability. It was
this hidden greed on the right side which our Lord Jesus so
frequently and sharply censured. The doctor often comes in touch
with money, and, usually, much of it. One should not hide from
oneself that there is seductive, demonic power inherent in money.
It is encountered both in profit and in the saving and use of
money. It often mixes unnoticed in our affairs, exercising influence, for example, on our conduct toward patients, on the
selection of preventive measures, on our joy in work, our willingness to be disturbed at night, etc.

Apart from special circumstances and causes, the doctor is, as
a Christian, I think, not in general obligated to have a con-
spicuously low standard of living. Of course he has no need to
take part in the usual race toward "all riches of the world and its
splendor." He possesses indeed an unspeakably rich treasure
hidden in his field. But generally he serves his neighbor much
more effectively if he also allows himself necessary recreation
and comfort without economizing too much, for example, in the
selection of a vacation spot, manner of travel, or of eating. Thus
he comes naturally into the danger of slipping away from the
authentic Christian center of living, in which a joyful willingness
for renunciation prevails. Nevertheless, in Christendom renunciation is not actually purpose itself, but only a means. Even then,
we should not generalize here, dogmatically. But do not these
renunciations of the doctor make sense, if he practices them, so
to speak, parallel with his specialty and with his natural place
in society by cheerfully sacrificing his night rest and his mealtime
in the case of need, or perhaps some important and very desirable
part of his planned daily program? Or by uncomplainingly
giving his energies and interests to offensive and troublesome
men? All this weighs much more than a debate on what standard of living is suitable in this type of work. Those patients whose
doctor must work under the pressure of economic burden and
sorrow are indeed unfortunate. This viewpoint deserves consideration in the case of the regulation and the working conditions
of doctors also.

Temptation encounters the doctor in a special form in the area
of holding back the speaking of truth. One of my teachers
once said, "Truth is like a naked lady. One should pay attention
to how and where one exposes her." Many interpret this as per-

mission, if not an obligation, to keep secret from the patient the type of illness he has and especially the nearness of death. The doctor sets himself forth thus as a lord over the truth and from his summit measures it out drop by drop for other men according to his discretion. Such behavior does not befit the Christian faith, where veracity is an absolute value and candor a genuine life-form. As a Christian the doctor is not permitted to lie. Nevertheless, it is not always necessary to tell the whole truth which one supposes to know. The deciding factor should be the well-being of the patient, not only his physical well-being but that of his entire person. If the doctor still prefers to remain silent, he should speak as a Christian about his patient to his Lord in secret. That is no empty pious fanaticism but simply recognizes that there is a superhuman power which is not inherent in weak man. Then he opens his ear to the spirit of love and truth in order to receive direction as to whether he should say a word or not. In any case, he should never deny the invisible contact with his Lord.

Maintaining faith is in many respects more difficult for the doctor than for many others. He must act in the case of examinations and professional decisions and think in the case of major crises as if everything depended on worldly deeds or causes. And indeed, every situation must be viewed according to the natural laws of God up to a certain boundary of our life's sphere. Beneath this boundary belongs the entire medical science and the thought world of the doctor as natural scientist. Here is seen his God-ordained profession. He must investigate and confirm everything immanent, explaining the possible errors and the cases of neglect. It has thereby been made more difficult for him to take everything in faith alone from the hand of God.

Yet faith looks deeper, and every day in the hearts of Christians it should and must brave the frontier of immanence. The doctor recognizes the higher hand which also moves his hand and brain. It is precisely this faith which permits the believing doctor no dispensation from conceptual work on the strictly terrestrial level. To be satisfied with living in the resultant tension is a continuing temptation which he can never escape. (2 Cor. 12:8). On the contrary, at this point, the answer which Paul receives to his constant complaint is appropriate: "My grace is sufficient for you."

SUSUMU AKAHOSHI, M.D.

Surgeon and Psychiatrist
Tokyo, Japan

Agape and Eros

In this short article I would like to discuss the problem of love from my viewpoint of psychopathology. I think this is suitable for this book which will be published for Dr. Paul Tournier, a man of love, on his seventy-fifth birthday.

First I will summarize my basic viewpoint of psychopathology in connection with the problem of love. I think I have recognized the fundamental importance of *basic mistrust* in psychopathology through my experiences in clinical psychiatry, especially of psychotherapy. I am of the opinion that basic mistrust is the fountainhead of all psychopathological phenomena, and that normal ego psychology is dominated also by basic mistrust.

By the term *basic mistrust* I mean the mistrust which is experienced by a baby in the mother-child relation during its first year, before the formation of its ego. Basic mistrust is a specifically human experience and has relation to the serious *dependency-need* of the human baby, based upon biological specialty of human beings. This specialty is pointed out by A. Portmann in his book *Biologische Fragmente zu einer Lehre vom Menschen.*[1] I would like to define the baby's experience of satisfaction of the dependency-need as its experience of basic trust, and the baby's experience of unsatisfied dependency-need as its experience of basic mistrust. E. Erikson has pointed out for the first time the importance of basic trust and basic mistrust in his book *Childhood and Society.*[2] He writes: "The first demonstration of social trust in the baby is the ease of his feeding, the depth of his sleep, the relaxation of his bowels." I think this is the experience of basic trust. However, afterwards in the same chapter he has confused basic trust and basic mistrust with secondary trust and secondary mistrust which are formed in the baby's ego after the baby has recognized its mother as another being.

I think that a baby comes to recognize its mother as another being through its experiences of basic mistrust. During and after the recognition of its mother (the formation of the baby's ego) we can observe two types of reaction which are both secondarily formed, being based upon basic mistrust. The one is a dependent reaction through which the baby persists in the satisfaction of its dependency-need, that is, it wants to indulge in the "desire to be loved" (*amae* in Japanese), in spite of its experience of basic mistrust. I call it *amae-reaction*, or *self-indulgence-reaction*. The other is a narcissistic reaction through which the baby makes primitive *self-supporting* efforts (*jiritsu* in Japanese) without persisting in the satisfaction of its dependency-need because of its severe experience of basic mistrust. I call it *jiritsu-reaction*, or *self-supporting-reaction*. It is obvious that the basic mistrust has been severer and deeper in the *jiritsu*-reaction than in the *amae*-reaction. These two types of reaction are always mixed in parallel in every baby, though the proportion of the mixture varies in each baby, and they work at every step of its development.

Sigmund Freud maintained that narcissism is the primary basic state of human beings, and desire to be loved is secondarily derived from narcissism. On the contrary, T. Doi, a Japanese psychoanalytic psychiatrist, asserts that desire to be loved is the primary basic desire (congenital instinctive desire), and narcissism is secondarily formed from the desire to be loved. Doi pointed out in his article "*Amae:* A Key Concept for Understanding Japanese Personality Structure"[3] that the Japanese word *amae* is adequate to express this instinctive desire. I think the *amae*-reaction is in content the same as Doi's *amae*, and the *jiritsu*-reaction is in content the same as Freud's narcissism. So, in contrast to both Freud and Doi, I myself think that both narcissism and *amae* are secondary reactions on the same level both based upon basic mistrust. This is the fundamental difference between their viewpoint and mine. I think this difference is due to the fact that Freud and Doi did not have insight into basic mistrust. It may be said that Freud built up his psychoanalysis starting from the *jiritsu*-reaction, and Doi built up his psychoanalytic psychopathology starting from the *amae*-reaction. I am attempting to build up a new theory of psychoanalytic psychopathology taking basic mistrust as the starting point.

Now, it is obvious that *amae* (desire to be loved) and narcissism are kinds of love, and we might give them the general name of *eros*. So we can say that *eros* is love which is secondarily formed, being based upon basic mistrust, in the baby's ego after the recognition of its mother. Thus *eros* has no connection with basic trust and is combined at the same level with secondary trust and secondary mistrust. I think that *eros*—*amae* and narcissism—is healthy when it is combined with secondary trust, and is pathological when it is combined with secondary mistrust. But however healthy they may be, both healthy *amae* and healthy narcissism are deeply rooted in basic mistrust and are inevitably ambivalent.

In contrast to *eros*, I think, *agape* is experienced in relation to basic trust. Basic trust which is experienced by the baby in mother-child relation before the formation of its ego is not acquired by the baby itself, but is a gift of its mother's love, which is spontaneous and unmotivated. Thus the mother's love in which her baby is experiencing basic trust partakes in the nature of *agape*, or at least points to *agape*, though every mother is an incomplete human being and her love is not a pure, complete *agape*. The Bible says of God's love: "In this is love, not that we loved God but that he loved us and sent his Son to be the expiation for our sins" (1 John 4:10). I should say of a mother's love: "In this is love, not that I loved my mother, but she loved me without any worthiness." A baby can experience basic trust only when it experiences such a mother's love.

After the formation of the baby's ego, however, mother-child relation becomes the relation between the child's ego and the mother's ego which is dominated by secondary trust and secondary mistrust, which are combined with *eros*. In ego psychology, that is, in psychology of *amae*-reaction and *jiritsu*-reaction, we cannot attain insight into basic mistrust, much less into basic trust. I think we can have insight into them only in true religious experience. Is not the Christian faith a basic trust in God's *agape*?

The Bible describes faith analogically in this way as a baby's basic trust in its mother's love: "Like newborn babes, long for the pure spiritual milk, that by it you may grow up to salvation" (1 Peter 2:2). "Truly, truly, I say to you, unless one is born anew, he cannot see the kingdom of God" (John 3:3).

This notwithstanding, we are apt to think that our secondary trust in God is true faith, without recognizing that true faith is basic trust in God. I think that is why the reformer Martin Luther warned us, saying: "Faith is not what men think faith is according to their own human illusory thoughts and dreams. . . . Rather faith is the act of God working within us" (Preface to the letter to the Romans). It is obvious that the faith of the Hellenistic religions is secondary trust in God, which is combined with *eros*. In the process of the Hellenization of Christianity, this Hellenistic faith, which is a mere secondary trust in God as an Absolute Being, has been mixed into the true Christian faith. A. Nygren wrote in his famous book *Agape and Eros* as follows: "In so far as the Eros motif forces its way into Christianity, we may speak of the Hellenisation of Christianity. This apparently introduces an idea which has long dominated the history of dogma, and recalls Harnack's well-known judgment: 'Dogma in its conception and development is a work of the Greek spirit on the soil of the Gospel.'" [4] I think the history of the theology of the Protestant Church has been a history of Hellenistic intellectualization of the gospel, and the faith of the Protestant Church has been apt to become secondary trust in God without being aware of it. Faith as secondary trust in God is the faith of the religion of *eros*. This is not true faith as basic trust in God, but is a mere belief as an act of the human ego which cannot avoid ambivalence. The decline of the Church in the present age is, I think, fundamentally due to the fact that our faith has become secondary trust in God. We must return to true faith as basic trust in God through experiencing God's *agape* in personal communion with the resurrected Christ.

Notes

1. Basel: Benno Schwabe, 1944.
2. New York: Norton, 1963.
3. In *Japanese Culture*, ed. Smith and Beardsley (Chicago: Aldine Publishing Co., 1962).
4. Philadelphia: Westminster Press, 1953.

HEINRICH HUEBSCHMANN, M.D.

Internal Medicine and Marriage Counselor
Heidelberg, West Germany

Concerning the Conscience of the Body

We are not accustomed to mentioning body and conscience in the same breath. The traditional Christian ethic in particular teaches us to see in conscience something purely spiritual. It considers conscience as the voice of God. However, God, so it teaches us, speaks to us only through our conscience. The body, as the embodiment of that which has nothing to do with conscience, has nothing to do with God speaking. It is even to be considered as the actual opponent of conscience. For a long time, the power which tarnishes the truth of conscience has been called the flesh.

The infernalness of the body found its end with the so-called Renaissance. But with natural science the body became a mere corpse, a governable, manipulable dead thing, a mechanical apparatus. It remained a mere servant of reason. Freud has also spoken of the body quite contemptuously. When Viktor von Weizsäcker applied the psychoanalytic method to organic illnesses (the *angina tonsillaris*) [1] and discovered an "organ language," i.e., the capacity of a body organ to behave itself spiritually, Freud was of the opinion, according to his analytical theory, that that was like the lord of the house's hatching a love relationship with the cook—certainly not to the advantage of the kitchen. He defended the toxic cause of sickness —thus pure somatogenesis. Freud was a Jew, but an emancipated Jew, and did not know that the Bible did not know anything of

38

the Greek separation of soul and body, but saw man as an animated body. Others had not forgotten that.

Pascal suggested "qu'on s'imagine un corps plein de membres pensants." [2] Georg Friedrich Hamann, the great opponent of Kant, seeing through the ambiguity of enlightened reason like a true Lutheran, knew about the spirituality of matter. "The entire corporal nature is an expression, a parable of the spiritual world." [3] "Nature and history are the two great commentaries of the divine word." [4]

Nietzsche turned against the "despisers of the body" and spoke of the "great reason of the body" against the "small reason which you call spirit." [5] This should not be misunderstood materialistically, but is intended against a *ressentiment*-laden conscience that does not partake of its actual needs.

Medicine has to do with the body which is taken ill. Sickness is a denial of life—damage, destruction. However, we will not see the patient and the illness rightly if we see only the defect. A truth reveals itself in the sickness, which, until that point, has been concealed from the patient and those around him. We experience that when we speak with the patient. A heart attack may be chosen as an example.

I have asked a great number of heart-attack patients in a heart sanitorium concerning the conditions of origin of their sickness. I was particularly interested in how they stood in their profession. They were mostly extraordinarily capable men and women. They affirmed their work, considered their activity to be meaningful, and were of the conviction that they held an important position in the business. They served well, and were content. But under this surface area were hiding emotions of an entirely different type. An individual case may illustrate that.

A fifty-four-year-old man has been active sixteen years as factory manager in a vulcanization plant. His duty consists in supervising a great number of workers in the repairing and renewal of auto tires. He looks after his job very conscientiously and is aware of his responsibility for the travel safety and the life of the automobile traveler. He is very polite and enjoys wide popularity with all auto travelers in the area. His highest satisfaction is to go home in the evening with a good conscience that everything is cared for and the factory is "safe." Nor does he hesitate at night or at the close of business to travel one hundred kilometers distant in order to come to the aid of a driver. It is thanks to his untiring effort that the number of customers and business of the undertaking are constantly increasing. He is an ideal manager and proud of his success. But his self-feeling is a mask behind which entirely different feelings are hiding. He is embittered over his lack of freedom. There are the customers. He is enraged over their demands. "The customer is king." He feels himself exploited.

And there is his boss. He, the manager, has made three inventions, and wanted to register them for patent. A large rubber factory offered DM 80,000. His boss demanded the inventions for himself, since they had been made in his factory, although he had scarcely lifted a finger concerning them.

Furthermore, the factory was taken over one day by a larger tire firm. The boss did not take the deserving manager into confidence, but told him only of the completed deed. The manager is indignant and feels himself sold like a piece of factory inventory.

But what does he do? Nothing. Concerning the demands of the customers, he doubles up his fist in rage, but only in his pocket. That someone has taken from him his three inventions and then finally sold them himself, he attempts to accept and to forget. When the little firm is swallowed by the greater, he seeks out individually in their residences the customers who have not returned in order to obtain them for the new firm.

The new large firm has 103 branches. Every year the sales leaders and work managers of individual branches gather together in a group at the main firm in order to render account. The branches are judged according to their sales and are compared to each other. Praise and blame are distributed according to points. Our manager sees it as his ambition to receive only praise.

In order to let this man "speak to his person," I pointed out to him that certainly the firm and its interests and he might be on opposite sides from each other. Surprised, he spoke, but not about his own feelings or complaints; rather, frightened, he answered, "You believe that I am not suited for this post?" He considered himself only through the eyes of the firm's leadership. It did not yet occur to him to stand off at a distance from his undertaking. What is happening here?

We have before us the widespread type of a man for whom the demands of the work world have become absolute. One does not merely serve the undertaking; one identifies himself with it. There is here a foreign determination which no longer allows any self-consciousness to emerge. The individual conscience is fully oppressed by the work conscience. There is no instance of anything transcending the work at hand. Or is there?

I explained to him that his work virtues are a symbol also, of compliance, and asked him whether he is a professional fool. He does not deny that and continues speaking of his father, a poor factory worker, who had also been so "good-natured," "a good father." Was the father always right? "No," and then he decided, "But he was the *father!*" He identified himself thus with the father, in spite of his criticism of him. I ask, "Was the father and is he thus the good Lord for you?" He replies, "Do not speak of the good Lord. Otherwise, I become irritable. The good Lord—if one names him, then one should not think in terms of speed of sound, but in light-years, so far is he removed." God is for him, it appears, practically not at hand.

Therefore I return to earth and ask whether he considers it to be the goal of his life that all men should be pleased with him. Then comes an answer which now actually startles me. "No, for me the saying by Klaus Störtebecker [a famous sailor] is sufficient: 'Friend of the good Lord and enemy of all men.'" Since I never again saw the patient, because he was shortly thereafter released from the sanitorium, I could not establish whether he had at any time earnestly followed this selected saying of his youth. His professional relationships were, in any case, exactly the opposite. He had sacrificed himself for the profit of strangers, but he had no developed awareness of that.

That attack occurred on a Sunday afternoon, when he had just returned from vacation, and was to begin work again. For a long time he had wanted to give notice but had been unable to accumulate enough capital—and the power of decision had failed him. He had not been able to save himself. Now, temporarily, his illness had forced him to that. His illness appears as the expression of a mute protest against the social pressures to which he had resigned himself. It was representative of the resistance of which his conscience was not capable. It shows itself as a bodily rising of the individual's existential conscience against the self-alienating servant conscience. It is as if the body itself remembered the selected saying of his youth and followed it, since his conscience had been unfaithful to him.

Notes

1. See Weizsäcker, "Die Körpergeschehen und Neurose," in *International Zeitschrift für Psychoanalyse*, v. 19, 1933; reprint, Stuttgart: Klett, 1947.
2. *Pensées*, fragment 473.
3. *Biblical Observations of a Christian.*
4. *Fragments.*
5. *Thus Spoke Zarathustra.*

JACQUES SARANO, M.D.

Gastroenterologist
Valence, France

Psychosomatics and Religion: Two By-Products of the Medicine of the Whole Person

To my physician friends I acknowledge a splinter in the flesh of the medicine of the whole person. A living dynamic, it can only be described and translated objectively in terms of the products of the decomposition of its cadaver: *psychology* and *religious or spiritual persuasion.*

In a book or a technical conference, the medicine of the whole person can only be propounded in terms of psychosomatics. This misunderstanding must be fought without letting go; break the shell to get to the almond; recapture, through the outer wrappings, the living inspiration; break open the safe of objectivity; participate in the experiment of subjective confrontation; in short, commune within a community such as ours.

Paul Tournier is inspired and inspires: the medicine of the whole person is not learned from manuals, but one can have the good luck to meet Paul Tournier.

The medicine of the whole person is not a technique, it is an encounter. If certain among us dreamed of building up a doctrine, a theory, a system, an anthropology of the medicine of the whole person, Paul Tournier was right in refusing to have any part in it: one has suffered too much from the "founders" of religion.[1]

Others make an effort to glean clinical observations from the medicine of the whole person. They are wasting their time. It has already been done somewhere under the heading of psychosomatics.

43

Can one define the medicine of the whole person? The person is perhaps someone whom I could call *thee* (in the sense of Martin Buber and G. Marcel, whose opposite is *him*), respect, and above all exchange with, sharing, beyond words to express, what is personal. The reciprocity of the relationship appears to be fundamental.

But have not all the psychotherapies put the emphasis, with Freud, on transfer and countertransfer? Do they not make me conscious of my own attitudes, my own person, even in the approach to and treatment of my patients?

While adopting as his own this "limited but considerable transformation of his personality" (Balint), the psychotherapist anxious to maintain his objective neutrality nevertheless practices a policy of "noninvolvement." The medicine of the whole person involves one entirely personally, it compromises itself sooner in the therapeutic relationship, at the same time avoiding falling into the trap of an ill-defined "apostolic" function, a paternalistic "humanitarian" attitude or some other unconscious and badly analyzed identification.

Let the technician or the psychologist have the triumphant satisfaction of describing symptoms, "talking around" the question or the situation. Our patients are as greedy as our colleagues: they want an explanation or a solution: they are disappointed. The doctor looking for an inquiry, a procedure, will not find it. Nothing. Stripped to the bone. Then perhaps an event—or an advent.

No explanation, no solution. A closer attention, a sharing. The medicine of the whole person is not so much knowing or knowing how as it is a way of being attentive and listening; not so much knowing as knowing how to be, nay, to involve oneself completely in the therapeutic relationship.

Experience has shown the impressive efficacy of listening, of personal exchange, of silence, of a way of being and the ensuing loosening up, the ripening conflict and finally the fall of an impregnable fortress, around which the employ of the most scholarly of techniques had accomplished nothing.

One may become a matchless psychotherapist, psychiatrist, or psychoanalyst and never reach the *person*. That is why psychiatrists and psychoanalysts come to us. Inversely, there are among us clinicians, surgeons, and laboratory researchers, who have not had training in psychotherapy. The medicine of the whole person avails itself of the organic and psychological techniques but does not stop there; it is not in the same order of things, nor does it pretend to take the place of them.[2]

The most elaborate psychotherapeutic techniques turn into stone before the problems of transfer and countertransfer if they are not enriched with the spirit and the exigencies of the medicine of the whole person, this "splinter in the flesh" which reminds us not to fall back upon the object-technique, which sees the patient as an object.

The medicine of the whole person, then, is not a new pharmaceutical or psychotherapeutical technique. Nor is it a Sunday psychology or a poor relation of specialists in the "sickness of the soul." And every time we get too smart, begin to proselytize, become didactic or scholarly, a cunning genius will reduce us to ashes: the *déja vu*, the good old everyday homespun psychology or worse: soul healing!

I scarcely dare say the word *disciple* of Paul Tournier. No, he is a presence, a splinter in our flesh, a challenge, a spirit. Let us agree that we have nothing to teach to anyone and that we will always be apprenticed to the medicine of the whole person.

A spiritual transformation under the auspices of organic and psychosomatic medicine: that, for me, is the medicine of the whole person.

Notes

1. Of Christ and the Good News, disciples and successors have made a new religion, a copy of the one which had been destroyed: dogmas, anathemas, theologies, inclusions, and exclusions.
2. Also, the spiritual exigencies of most practitioners of the medicine of the whole person could not take the place of a solid technical education.

THEODORE BOVET, M.D., Th.D.

Psychiatrist and Marriage Counselor
Zürich, Switzerland

Person and Ideology

We all live in the midst of ideologies—political, social, religious, and philosophical. We are engaged and challenged by them. We must discuss with them, and we are in that way called into question as persons.

The *person* is a mysterious, created totality which lives standing in relationship with other persons: man and woman, I and thou, God and man. A relationless, closed monad is no person. Indeed, one can define a person frankly as a "junction of relations," as one has defined the smallest element of matter as a junction of energy waves.

An essential mark of the person is that it does not develop as all physical or chemical processes, according to a predetermined time-plan which can be measured quantitatively by some clock; rather, every living being possesses a specific duration in which it changes itself qualitatively from moment to moment. The physical time which we measure with our clocks is always uniform. The organic duration, on the other hand, is a qualitative measure, different for every living being and for it as specific as its space-form. One speaks therefore also of the "time-form" of an organism and means its entire development in the course of duration. Henri Bergson, who first discovered this fundamental difference between quantitative and qualitative duration, speaks of the "actual" or "creative duration" (*durée réelle ou durée créatrice*). Every individual moment varies from one species to the next. With man, the shortest perceptible moment amounts to 1/18 of a second; with the snail it amounts, on the contrary, to 1/4 of a second; then with the very fast fighting fish to only 1/30 of a second. Lecomte du Noüy spoke of the "granulated time" (*le temps granulaire*) which stipulates different experiences for every species.

On the other hand, what is an *ideology?* The expression was coined in 1796 by Destutt de Tracy, who wanted to investigate the formulation of ideas out of biologically and sociologically derived sensations. Karl Marx led this investigation further in deriving convictions of a particular group from the economic situation and thereby relativizing them. The best-known example: religion is no absolute revealed truth, but it is a compensation of the fantasy for the real sorrow in which the majority of men live. It enables them to endure the pressure; it is the "opium of the people." It is in the interest of the ruling classes to propagate religion so that they can further exploit the masses of people without their rebelling. Thus Marx means by ideology a class-bound mode of feeling, a self-interested prejudgment which, conscious or unconscious, serves the advantage of the concerned class. To be sure, the use of the word today is so generalized that "ideology" does not mean only the false mode of feeling of the enemy, coined through class-conditioned prejudice, but at the same time also the individual, natural correct view. But if one subsequently thinks as a Marxist, then one will set every class- or group-conditioned *Weltanschauung* under ideological thought, since it apparently will further the interests of this class or group.

There are, however, objective, formal criteria for unmasking a *Weltanschauung* as an ideology. According to Hans Freyer,[1] ideologies build themselves up on several small presuppositions and they disregard or suppress the entire fabric of reality, which exists without regard to the presuppositions. Thus they also do not take man seriously as a person, but set him as a function, as an "individual" in their system. While science is always ready to revise its theories when an experiment refutes it, ideology selects only the facts which substantiate its theory, remaining silent on the other hand concerning the contradictory, or explaining it as a malicious distortion of reality. Thus research in all ideological lands stands under strict control. Nothing may be discovered which contradicts the fundamental dogma. Of a necessity the researcher is prevented from doing harm. Thus the Catholic ideology acted against Giordano Bruno or Galilei; thus the French Revolution beheaded their uncomfortable thinkers; it happened thus in the Third Reich, and happens still in the U.S.S.R. Every ideology is summarized in several clear, incontrovertible sentences, which the broad masses will accept as *the* absolute truth. Whoever doubts is a heretic. To every ideology the heretic belongs as the shadow to the light, and where one speaks of heresy, there is an ideology.

A great danger of most ideologies is that they arise from the ground of authentic truths. Out of the ground of the living message of the gospel have arisen a whole series of "Christian" ideologies, whose differences apparently were postulated sociologically and psychologically. Since each of them makes the claim to the absolute and unique saving truth, they must accuse opponents of heresy, and fight them bloodily even though the strife was only concerning an iota. On the basis of the humanism of Karl Marx, the dogmatic "Marxism" and "Marxism-Leninism" arose where millions of heretics were "liquidated," and the humanist-socialism of "Prague-spring" had to be put down with tanks. Karl Marx should have said at the end of his life, "En tous cas moi, je ne suis pas marxist" ("In any case, I am not a Marxist"). Jesus might well also say, "In any case, I am not Catholic, not Lutheran, not Reformed, not Orthodox, but I died for all of you so that some day you might mend your ways."

The ideology which threatens us all the most since it is not itself presented as ideology is the middle-class culture in which we live. Its main dogmas may well be: individualism, liberalism, private property, free enterprise, and, flowing from that, capitalism and imperialism. This ideology is not so closed and is not characterized as such at first glance as communism or fascism, but its secret power over man is scarcely any less, and it can in individual cases work even more inhumanly.

How do we behave now as persons over against ideologies? In 1936 Emanuel Mounier in his periodical *Esprit* published a "Manifeste au Service du Personnalisme" that still is worthy of reading. He resisted the making of this "personalism" into a new ideology. But it also did not come to be the great movement to which he called. Perhaps it functions not actually as a great popular movement but in the action of many individuals who as resistance fighters, each in his own place, defend the person against ideology.

Before everything else, the following realizations appear important: the "person" as created totality is something basically different than the "individual," which means simply the smallest entity of the mass. A society of persons is like a union of cells of a living organism; a mass of individuals is on the other hand to be compared to a sandpile or a sandstone. As doctors, educators, pastors, industrial psychologists, it is always our first obligation to point again towards that. As soon as a form of society, an educational system, a political or religious movement begins to be "ideologized," i.e., made into a closed system in itself, incontrovertible, and a system which alone saves, it becomes inhuman, at enmity with the person, and we must fight it. This should not be treated as a negative battle against some "ism" or else this will easily become an ideology itself. Much more is it the positive battle *for* the person, for personal encounter—thus the true love— between man and woman, parents and children, employers and employees, and representatives of various cultures and races. This personal relationship will today best be expressed by the word *partnership,* although it is a somewhat worn-out term. Apparently one should say that partnership and ideology exclude one another. Partnership respects the secret of the person, its inner freedom, and its never exactly calculable development in creative duration.

In this battle of freedom, the medicine of the whole person delivers concrete experiences, realistic definitions, and constructive criticisms, which give to the personalism beheld by Mounier a new and good face that is nearer to reality.

Notes

1. *Theorie des gegenwärtigen Zeitalters* (Stuttgart: 1955).

GERRIT A. LINDEBOOM, M.D.

Professor of Internal Medicine
Free University
Amsterdam, Holland

The Crumbling Foundations of Medical Ethics

*To Paul Tournier, the champion of the highest
Christian standards in medical practice*

At the present time there is small need of any demonstration that medical ethics is confronted by an acute crisis and has been brought into an embarrassing state of uncertainty. It will be sufficient simply to refer to the radical changes in the attitude to abortion—particularly to an abortion performed on social grounds—which is now widespread in the medical professions of many lands. It is a sure sign of the profound change in attitude to medical ethics and the general loss of those convictions which have controlled medical thinking and action for more than two thousand years.

It is no doubt significant that, until the publication some ten years ago of the third edition of its handbook on medical ethics, the Royal Association of Physicians of the Netherlands declared moral standards to be grounded in eternal principles. When the edition sold out in the ordinary course the Association delayed the issue of a fourth edition. Recently, however, it was decided to issue the contents in loose-leaf form. It would appear that over a period of ten years ethical standards have become so indeterminate that they are as readily interchangeable as the leaves of the book.

Medical ethics, which is only a specialized section of ethics as

50

a whole, received its earliest and normative codification from Ancient Greece. Its origins were not in the Bible. In fact, neither in the Old Testament or the New Testament do we find distinct principles or formulations of medical ethics.

In the oath of Hippocrates (born *ca.* 460 B.C.), the chief rules for ethical conduct were laid down for the medical practitioner. It was much later, several centuries after the struggle between Christ and Aesculapius, that a settlement in favor of the Christian faith led to the Christianizing of medical ethics by invoking the God and Father of Jesus Christ in place of Apollo.

Since that time there has been much common agreement among doctors concerning the principal lines of medical ethics, whether these were based on humanitarian considerations or on distinctive Christian belief. In day-to-day affairs, the ethics of the humanist and of the Christian have tended to converge when it comes to practical action. Then there came abrupt and tragic violation of those principles under the Nazi régime. After the liberation, the World Medical Association in 1948 adopted and sent to its member national societies the Declaration of Geneva. In it were restated, brought up to date, and strengthened the main principles of the Hippocratic oath.

The influence of this oath down the centuries has proved quite incalculable. It has served as an international code which has guided and buttressed the medical profession in an unshakable belief in the highest values of human life. It has brought to medical practitioners a sense of dignity and solidarity in their work. It has inspired and guaranteed the confidence of the public in those whose duty it has been to treat and care for sick persons. It was because these medical ethical rules were grounded in a supernatural revelation, or in the enduring common values of humanity, that the same earlier authors would write of the "divine" origin of medicine.

It is true that a constantly overworked and overburdened individual practitioner may often have found little time, and may have lacked the inclination, to reflect much upon the basis of his professional ethics. But in most cases he accepted these standards, even when he failed to uphold them. The central concept was the sanctity of life or, in the words of Albert Schweitzer, "reverence for life."

How has it come about that this traditional structure could

have been so extensively undermined in recent years? There have been a number of factors which have each contributed to the present threatening situation. It is not possible in the short space of a dedicatory essay to discuss and evaluate them all. Three main groups of influences may, however, be clearly distinguished.

First, there are the rapid technical developments in medicine, which have made possible what to earlier workers would have seemed miraculous advances. There have been additional possibilities in attempts at resuscitation, extreme measures to prolong life, more sophisticated techniques for preserving lives which already have become subhuman and mutilating operations to "save" for a short time a life which already in principle has been lost. All of these—and other similar measures—have had the effect of weakening the practitioner's sense of obligation to preserve life in the more familiar situation. While for themselves the majority of physicians may not yet feel doubt at these points, yet more of them have begun to feel, at least, uncertain. This uncertainty arises from the sensitive heart of medicine and the human feelings of the physician.

Secondly, there are undeniably the results of the growing impact of modern society on medical practice. The public has come to expect too much—almost everything—from science and medicine. It is no longer willing to consider itself as underage or untrained for these things. It wants to have its say in all matters concerning the health and lives of its members. Moreover, while our Western culture still bears the evidences of its earlier Christian upbringing, it is rapidly developing in a direction which will become more and more remote from its earlier sources of inspiration. This process in a society which "has come of age" is proceeding with increasing speed.

Major elements in these developments in recent times have been the emancipation of women and the widespread revolution in attitudes to sex. There is now an increasingly vociferous demand for complete sexual freedom. Monogamous marriage as the fundamental basis for our community life is under increasingly heavy attack. The assertion of a "right" to sex relations in the absence of true love, together with a "right" to uninhibited homosexual behavior, has promoted a promiscuity which is being more widely condoned or even recommended. There can be

no longer any doubt that we are members of a permissive society in which pornography, male and female prostitution,
adultery, and abortion have come to be regarded as of positive
value to the community or even as a necessity for personal happiness. In such a context no reverence for life—either in its
early or late phases—can be expected where it comes to be regarded as in the way of the convenience and happiness of others.

A third category is to be found in recent theoretical developments and changes of attitude in the spheres of philosophical
and theological ethics.

Ethics in general is becoming increasingly based upon the
philosophy of evolutionism. At the outset the theory of evolution
was chiefly concerned with the origins of life, but now it has
become a dogma which serves as the basic principle in an all-embracing philosophical system, which sets out to account for the
world and the whole of life. Biology—studying the behavior of
other mammals—is considered to provide important inspiration
for the conduct of human life. What is now regarded as "ethical"
is that which is useful to society. The ethics of evolutionism has
become, in principle, social ethics assessed according to its
usefulness and support of human "rights."

It is important here to notice that, at least in the country best
known to the writer, Christian ethics is also developing in a
direction of transition from personal to social ethics. For two
thousand years theology was the inspiration and guardian of
Christian ethics. The standards for man's moral conduct were
derived from the Holy Scriptures. Attention was paid not only
to the Ten Commandments, but also to the entire teaching of
both the Old and New Testaments. At the present time, however,
there appears to be a growing tendency to restrict biblical
ethical principles to the double commandments "to love" in our
Lord's summary of the Law and the prophets often known as
"the Golden Rule." Several theologians, who would regard themselves and be regarded as orthodox, now assert that these
two commands are sufficient to support a truly Christian approach
to the problems of euthanasia, sexual freedom, abortion, and
homosexuality. The lessons which former generations of Christians drew from other parts of the Bible are considered as ir-
relevant because they are founded upon what are now regarded
as historical records. The validity and relevance of these inci-

dents and teachings are regarded as no more than those of any such examples from past history.

This transformation of personal into social ethics is one more evidence of the underlying shift from "verticalism" to "horizontalism" in theology. The place of supernatural revelation and divine providence has been usurped by human experiment and experience. Ethical standards are more and more derived from colleagues working on the horizontal plane. No longer do we have eternal rules revealed by divine inspiration and in control of man's moral behavior. It is suggested that the rules for our conduct in present conditions can only be discovered and formulated in consultations between different faculties and fields of research. A multidisciplinary approach has to guarantee the validity of the ethical answer to the complicated problems of man's moral behavior. It is evident that the preaching of this gospel will result essentially in a reduction in acceptance of the Bible's teaching concerning the metaphysical aspects of ethics. Moreover, the aggregate of all these partial approaches neither validates nor adds up to an adequate approach to the problem as a whole.

Hence, in addition to the internal tensions in medicine, which arise from technical advances and which also endanger the doctor-patient relationship, there are these other main factors. Combining to precipitate a crisis in medical ethics are the pressures from a secularized society and the collapse by default of theological ethics. The resultant danger is one which is fundamental.

On the other hand, at the present time, there seems to be a new and increasing awareness of the dangers inherent in the loss of an ethical handhold. It is probable that medical ethics is being studied, reflected on, and discussed more widely than ever before. Even students are beginning to request lectures on medical ethics.

The starting point of a Christian's approach to medical ethics must be his view of man as a person. The key principle in the Bible's teaching is that each life (however obscure may be the individual) is a living entity which has meaning and eternal value. Suffering, too, is not meaningless in a Christian perspective. Hence, the Christian physician should be ready to listen first to the voice of God in Holy Scripture, then to the voice of his conscience, and only after *that* to the deliberations of a multidisciplinary discussion. It may be that it is only a medical practitioner, who has learned to accept personal grief as coming from God's fatherly hand, who will be able to understand fully the Christian approach to the embarrassments and distressing problems of medical ethics in our times.

For over twenty years, annual weeks for meditation have been arranged by Dr. Paul Tournier and his *équipe* ("team"). His daily talks from the Bible at the beginning of each day's discussions have opened God's revelation and thrown spotlights upon many aspects of medical ethics. In Tournier's concept of the *médecine de la personne* certain requirements stand out in relief. They are the personal attitude of the physician to God and to his fellow-man, the need for daily personal conversation with the Lord, and the religious background between the doctor and his patients.

Tournier may not be the man—nor is it probable that he would wish—to write a formal textbook of medical ethics as viewed from a Christian standpoint. Yet there are very few men at the present time who are bringing such a welcome and helpful approach to a medical practitioner's day-to-day contacts with, and duty to, his patients.

May God grant our friend Tournier yet many more years of inspiring activity in the service of our Lord and in promoting the spiritual well-being of the medical profession.

EWARTS G. LOOMIS, M.D.

General Practitioner and Psychotherapist
Hemet, California

A Retreat for "Médecine de la Personne"

In the past, the practice of medicine has been disease-oriented—reality accorded to a disease, but not to the "person" who is ill. The new medicine, *médecine de la personne,* must be less concerned with the peripheral effects of disease and more intently involved with the individual and his inner struggle, i.e., the time-space bound egocentric self against the real self which is timeless, without form. Dramatic world changes are affecting man's evolution, his concepts, and his institutions. The future focus must be upon centers for healing where a concept of the medicine of the whole person will promote health through the healing of the inner man rather than the mere eradication of disease.

As the word implies, disease is a state of consciousness without ease or peace of mind. Similarly, the French *maladie* and the German *Krankheit* imply a lack of harmony within the person. Real issues are not faced if the cause of disease is sought from the entry of bacteria or other foreign agents into the body, or from the inborn or acquired metabolic failures, while overlooking the disharmony within the person which is found in illness. When disease is dealt with as though it came from without rather than from within, the patient is deprived of the opportunity of honestly facing himself. This form of treatment deals with secondary effects of a state of malfunction rather than a search for the cause. It is necessary, as Paul Tournier points out in his book *The Healing of Persons,* to make two diagnoses: one, the usual medical diagnosis; the other, the diagnosis which includes factors of the intimate life of the patient.

When all the factors are evaluated properly, a more accurate diagnosis can be made—one which will be less descriptive of physical and psychological appearances and more concerned with the message of the human being as expressed symbolically through the signs and symptoms of illness. Treatment will not emphasize the mere restoration of the physical being with the ability to function more adequately within the framework of society, but rather, it will promote a feeling of inner peace and certitude within the human soul through a recognition of its unique place in the universe and its total relationship to the whole of life. The outward appearance of the physical body and the substance of man's communication will thus be recognized as a mirroring of the inner man. It is the inner man who needs to be healed in a deeper way than is possible when he is an outpatient for a short time. True healing requires adequate time in a nurturing environment.

Toward the goal of providing a nurturing environment with a live-in, family setting where there would be time for healing, a research center, "Meadowlark," was founded in Hemet, California, in 1957. Taking advantage of Southern California's superb climate, it has been possible to provide a retreat-type atmosphere the year around for approximately twenty-five persons simultaneously. From the moment the guest steps onto the spacious grounds he is greeted by the soothing green of growing plants, trees, flowers, and lawn. He becomes acutely aware of the nurturing warmth, and the abundance of life provided by nature. Here the inner man can be healed while specific attention is focused upon the whole man, physically, mentally, emotionally, and spiritually.

The new guest is given a welcoming packet, introducing a new way of life with concepts for living which will challenge him. Included with information about the staff, the program, and the facilities is a questionnaire which asks pertinent questions: physical disabilities; daily routines; musical, literary and color preferences; religious affiliations; experiences with prayer or meditation and the presence of God; and goals, which should include the desire for recovery and health. The physical examination given at the medical center is directed toward the restoration of harmony within the person rather than being oriented towards disease. The human being who is temporarily out of tune with the universe is carefully assessed. A nutritional survey and a careful examination for any endocrine deficiencies are made along with a five-hour glucose tolerance test which may bring to light hypoglycemia.

Hypoglycemia seems to be one of the most commonly met states of imbalance, and most frequently unrecognized problems of the prediabetic state, regularly associated with poor eating habits, the overuse of stimulants and devitalized foods, and the stresses brought to bear mentally and emotionally upon the patient. Thus, emphasis is placed on frequent feedings of natural food products. Menus include whole grain cereals, raw fruits and vegetables, unsaturated, non-hydrogenated fats, and herb teas along with protein-rich foods. Organically grown foods are used whenever obtainable. White flour, white sugar, coffee and tea are avoided. Guests become aware of the necessity of caring for their bodies.

To augment body conditioning, a program has been designed to include relaxation techniques and exercise. The importance of exercise receives particular attention for conditioning the heart, lowering blood pressure, improving diabetes, reducing weight, strengthening weak backs, relieving arthritic conditions, etc. Suggested program includes walking, jogging, cycling, swimming, and hiking at least five days a week. The importance of finding one's natural rhythm is stressed, as exercise in a state of constant tension defeats its own purpose. It is much better to allow the limbs to find their own rhythm and flow with it than to force them. According to the Bible, "they that wait upon the Lord shall renew their strength; they shall mount up with wings as eagles; they shall run and not be weary; and they shall walk and not faint" (Isa. 40:31). Walking is the first scheduled activity of the day. The freshness of the morning and the stirring of all life are excellent preparations for the half-hour spent in the chapel where each worships in his own way. The individual heart of the worshiper receives its own message.

After a hearty breakfast, three hours are devoted to self-discovery through the release of body tensions and mental knots. Because of the rapid-moving, manipulative culture of the times,

few are aware of their state of tension which is a block to creative forces. The first hour is devoted to loosening up individual
groups of muscles so their natural resilience may be refound. In
our highly structured, competitive culture, the "me-mine" state
of mind tends to dominate, submerging the "I-Thou" relationship. In so doing, there is a generalized, unconscious tightening
of musculature to resist much of the outside world rather than a
receptive, welcoming, open state of mind and body. This resistance tends to separate one from his surroundings. Frequently,
it is the beginning of illness and premature aging. Thus, relaxation of body is primary.

Following body relaxation, there is a guided, meditative type
of mental relaxation which ends with music for reflection. While
the relaxed, open state of body and mind is acute, the individual
is given pastel colors and paper or a piece of clay to express
through an art medium his deepest feelings. Frequently, movement to music provides guests with the opportunity to express
the rhythm now surging through their bodies.

Evenings are spent in groups around the fireplace or on the
screened porch as the weather dictates. Here group encounter
through dialogue provides the opportunity for self-examination
and a keener awareness of others. Educational movies, special
music and tapes, and study of great literature, including the
Bible, help enlarge the understanding of the guests. There is a
special emphasis throughout the various portions of the program
upon the opportunities for growth and increased awareness
which may be found during illness and while enmeshed in life's
problems.

In summary and conclusion, it is the goal of wholeness and
health which must be promoted during illness rather than the
eradication of the symptoms of disease. The whole man must be
healed in a nurturing environment without a time limit, or
other restricting factors, being put upon him. A reuniting of
man with man, man with his environment, and man with God
must prevail. More healing centers are needed to incorporate
healing for all the fàcets of man.

The healing of a patient is described in her own words after
she experienced a period for recuperation in the atmosphere at
Meadowlark. The thoughts she expresses came to her as she sat
quietly in the little garden chapel:

I see the candle flames and flower arrangements, but all these tremulous awarenesses, including that of my own unsteadiness and frailty, are lost in the peace that breathes through me. I am somehow humming at a higher vibration and am caught up in a single yearning like the candle flames—that where my consciousness leaves off, the visible life and the love of God begins. So it is no longer hazardous to live at this edge of feeling, this precipice of self-abandonment. For it is only through the plunge of self through all its modes of knowing and feeling that one discovers one can live the life of the higher Self in a new element, and neither be suffocated nor lost, but forever found and safe. There would have been a time when I would have thought these words blasphemous, but not now. God uniting with me creates the *Inner Christ,* an embodiment of prayer, or a sustained man–God relationship.

HERBERT FRANK, M.D.

Internal Medicine
Stuttgart, West Germany

My Path to Medicine of the Whole Person

The development of man into a person is of particular importance for the doctor. He himself becomes a health technician if he recognizes and appreciates only the "case" and not the person of his patient. Without recognizing in his fellow-man the characteristics of a subject capable of making judgments, he would at the same time have to deny himself the capability of making judgments. This is true also for the pure natural scientist who can succeed with no objective judgment without lifting the claim himself to be a competent person. The following study I would like to present therefore in free literary form, an autobiographical contribution to the question of the origin of the person. Psychologically seen, the "case" offers always the possibility of gathering and comparing at hand special experiences of the "material."

The wind is impudent. I am on vacation, lying in the sand dunes at the sea. It is marvelous weather. The loose pages lie before me. There comes the whoosh of the wind and carries them, three, four, into all the four winds. I catch them all again, and the one which flew the farthest off the dune shall be the first upon which I inscribe thanks to Paul Tournier, revered and beloved friend. The lines I write will be a contribution to his seventy-fifth birthday, which all friends of the medicine of the whole person anticipate may come to him with the best of health.

Paul Tournier and the medicine of the whole person have played a significant role in my life. How that came to pass I want to tell him today. However, in order to describe the path which led me to the practice of personal medicine, I must go far back to understand and to encounter it in reality.

My memory reaches far back into earliest childhood. I saw colors. They were bright and moved before my eyes, to and fro, to and fro, sometimes darker, then again lighter. Suddenly shadows moved by. Then I winced and felt the fright move through my small body, from my head to the tips of my fingers and toes. I did not know that I lay in a baby carriage in the garden, that there were branches which moved before my eyes in the wind, and birds flying over whose voices I could hear but could not yet bring into connection with the passing shadows in the sky overhead. But apart from the fright, I felt well. I enjoyed the light, the brightness of the sky, the moving colors, and felt myself to be very fortunate and thankful. Naturally I did not yet know the words for this, even the little words *sky*, *branches*, and *bird*. They were nothing more than a kaleidoscopic picture, so beautiful, so blissful, so unique—truly the first revelation for me of the world and its beauty and the blissful feeling of fortune. I felt with my entire body the full hope of growth, a creature of nature like everything which encircled me, and I was at one with it. There was no inner and outer. I was together with everything—everything me, everything mine.

My childhood, which fell in the time of the First World War, was full of secret fears of the human and inhuman. I remember exactly one afternoon when I was eight years old. It was summer, and outside there glowed a yellow sky. The tip of the church tower, the St. Andreas Church, in which I was told I had been baptized, was just visible from the window. From my high position I looked out into the tops of the trees of the church plaza —the high lindens—and under them to the garden of my parents and the neighbors' houses. Swallows flew everywhere with jubilant cries.

It was very hot here under the roof. I had no desire to play, and every movement was an effort. My glance turned inward, for I had a problem, the most pressing of all there can be— whether or not there was a God, whether everything which played outside and took place was also reality; indeed, whether

I myself in my existence, with all my perceptions, was an accident, or whether God had willed and created all this, even myself.

I felt in myself the brooding melancholy of denial, the abyss of unfaith, and the despair lying there before me: everything accidental, senseless, miserable, a base deception of the mind! If he were everywhere and directed the fate of life, then he could also be here and give me a sign—he could so direct the flight of a bird that he could give an answer to my question— whether there was a creator and sustainer of everything, whether behind the appearances of things there was the acting God. And I prayed to him, and placed the question: if now *one* swallow would fly over in the section of sky which I could see then this would be a sign from him that he had understood my question; if not, then he did not exist.

I trembled with excitement when I counted to three and saw that no swallow flew over. I was deeply terrified. Then the answer was: He did not exist. At the same time I felt in the strangest way a deep peace over the answer. It would have been too cheap to see the swallow flying. God does not treat us so simply. I felt instead of this something quite different: the fortunate possibility to be able to choose myself between faith and unfaith in God.

For the first time, I experienced the freedom to be able to decide for myself, even in the territory of faith. I realized that it lay in *me* to want to believe, or also, not. The swallows could fly as they wanted. I was not dependent on them, nor was anything at all in my relationship to God and to the world which I so very much loved for the sake of its beauty. It was a good feeling to be free.

It was too hot here upstairs. Certainly it would be cooler downstairs, on the floor where we lived. So I told myself to overcome my laziness, to get up and go downstairs. To make such decisions and to carry through with them had been very difficult for me earlier. They originated to a certain degree by themselves and without my doing. Often I felt myself tired and exhausted, just as now; but all at once that was scarcely a problem at all. My body was tired, to be sure, but it obeyed me immediately when I simply wished. Thus I had the experience that in a certain way my personality was quite independent of

my body. Certainly I wanted it to obey me and felt fully fortunate that it stood at my disposal, if only I presented my desires
precisely, and immovably enough.

At twelve years old, I was a Boy Scout when I was asked
seriously for the first time which profession I had thought of
choosing. It was customary in the youth movement of that day
in Germany to look somewhat pitiably on the church and to make
fun of it. Nevertheless, to my own surprise I replied spontaneously that I wanted to be a pastor. When I was asked why, I
gave this answer: because I found the church such a sad place,
so far from life, and so in need of reform. To my great astonish-
ment, this explanation was immediately accepted and I was
wished good luck on the way. Certainly it was meant that the
path I had set before myself would not be easy.

A little later I experienced my confirmation with all the fervor
and depth of feeling of which youth is capable. But strange to
say, the need of putting my expressed plan into effect subsided,
and it was my very religiosity which stood in the way. I felt that
it would be hopeless to bring it to development in the framework
of the traditional ecclesiastical possibilities. The task was too
great and my powers for it were too small for such a life's choice.
I did not despise the church but I felt with great certainty that
this was not the place where I would like to settle down to
follow an inner vocation.

I was not yet quite seventeen years old when I was selected
to play Tasso for the large school celebration at the hundredth
anniversary of Goethe's death. Good theater productions belonged
to the tradition of our school. What may have induced my Greek
teacher, Dr. H., to select me for the part, I do not know. Certainly
he was an acquaintance of my parents and a patient of my
father. He had seen the puppet theater which I had built when
I was small, and had even been present at one of those sketched-
out productions when he and his wife had come for coffee. Later
I found out by chance that he had said then that he felt I had a
certain similarity to Goethe's youth portraits.

Perhaps it was simply his intuition to choose me, but what
was the effect on me? At the beginning, I remained cool during
the reading rehearsals. But when I had memorized my part and
began the first acting attempts, I stood suddenly as under
stress. Something had been ignited in me. Indescribable feelings

flowed together and changed my entire being. Spirit and emotion, language and feelings blended into one. There were no longer any inhibitions. I began to act on the plane of a higher existence. The law of the representative role had grasped me and worked through me, revealing itself. The production was given twice.

> With this kiss joins a tear,
> And consecrates the past.

I had no need to make this true. My face was overflowing with tears when I spoke it. Even my mathematics teacher had felt it when he, smiling, congratulated me after the performance. Naturally I was pleased about it, but in reality it did not matter at all. I was full of Tasso, captured and inspired by Goethe. I had grasped what is called standing up for a cause and living for a duty.

I loved literature and art in general. I read much, sketched and painted, designed costumes for school productions and played theater—Shakespeare, Kleist. Here I felt myself at home. With religious devotion, I hoped one day to live in this profession as actor and producer. I was already learning roles by heart, since I could not wait to play them: Leonce and Lena, Faust and Mephistopheles, Hamlet and Peer Gynt. I completed a qualifying exam at the theater, and waited for the future—and then came the Third Reich.

A year after that I passed the final exams and afterward completed labor service in an old marine barracks on the coast of the North Sea. I learned to drill and became acquainted with the whole melancholy of the soldier's life. I had to stand guard with a loaded rifle. I let myself endure joining an S.A. Paramilitary Physical Training Camp on the Baltic Sea, in order to get permission for further studies. For me it was terrible. We had to shoot at human dummies and were treated disgracefully. Several comrades committed suicide. I escaped misery through a request for examination. Without returning I went home to my parents and lay in bed, at the end of my strength. The family doctor came and did me a saving favor with his certificate which I submitted to the leader of our camp. His anger must have been frightful, as I later learned, but at the moment, in any case, I had been saved.

There was one thing I now knew with certainty—that any dreams of an artistic profession were finished since, quite simply, there was going to be a war. Subsequently there was no longer a question of my being permitted to study without a discharge certificate from the camp. It was much more difficult to escape the new obligations for accommodation of students in an S.A. home or other mass quarters or to avoid being blackmailed into becoming a member of a Nazi organization.

Fortunately no one had taken me into service with the examination. I had firmly decided in case of a coming war to live on the side of humanity against the powers of destruction. There was no other choice for me than to become a doctor.

The study of medicine was not easy for me. During the dissection courses, I acquired a severe stomach neurosis. For my sensitive artistic nature, corporeality and spiritual expression were one and the same. The constant wounding of my aesthetic feelings made me sick. At the time I believed I was incurably sick, so miserable did I feel. My life was passive. That was my misfortune. I had selected medicine in order not to have to abandon mankind and to be able to survive, not just because it was less dangerous than being a soldier—under the circumstances that was not the case—but simply because it was not my nature to shoot at men. Had I been forced to do that, I would have directed the first shot at myself, I had firmly decided.

In other ways also, my secret attitude toward men made my path difficult. Without letting myself be recognized externally, I heard nonetheless what was spoken around me—how they scoffed and laughed at men of my type, also how materialistic natural science strove to persecute us, or also to cast suspicions from the perspective of psychiatry. Thus there were times in which I began to doubt my own mind, and in complete loneliness, I feared that I had a psychosis. I felt deepest sympathy with the psychotics and empathized with the neurotic, about whom the majority of my colleagues were only amused.

To be able to endure the materialistically oriented science at the university, I attempted to enlarge my knowledge. In addition to my medical studies, I also heard lectures on theology, philosophy, psychology, art history, and journalism. I had a circle of worthwhile friends, male and female students from all departments with whom I was in essential unity. In common we rejected the political system in Germany and held the vague hope that it must somehow be possible to bring natural scientific knowledge into harmony with the ethical, religious positions of our inner lives. We lived and worked for ourselves, often discussing our problems all night long, and were therefore in great danger politically. We cooked our soup on a powder keg. Thus the years flew by: Göttingen, Freiburg, Munich, Rostock, and again Freiburg in Breisgau.

I had just been notified of the last examination when the Second World War began. Immediately I returned from my holiday with my parents to Freiburg, in order to complete my accelerated exam there. In February 1940, with my exam in hand, I was drafted as a medical orderly and remained a soldier until the end of the war and my imprisonment. There followed years of greatest personal isolation in dangerous artistic work, in poetry and painting, whose discovery would have meant certain death for me. Paris—Rouen—Dijon—return to Germany and secret friendships with persons of forbidden organizations, and finally the end of the war. I met my wife, and still did not have a complete medical education when I married. Now the point was to establish a means of livelihood as quickly as possible. Since during the war I had worked in surgical, but mainly in bacteriological, units, it was of primary importance to expand my knowledge in the area of internal medicine. Thus I became an assistant doctor in an internal ward in Stuttgart, finished my dissertation which I had not been able to complete during the war, and received recognition as a specialist in internal medicine.

I would gladly have become a psychotherapist, since I had recognized very early how greatly clinical medicine of this type had been neglected. I knew how many patients exposed the secret of their illnesses only after deep personal conversation, many times consciously but also many times not. I had witnessed wonderful cures at my station through such conversations with patients, but my position was considered unscientific among colleagues. After constant struggling to establish good contact with them, I finally won their belated approval only after many years. All the same, my distinguished teacher, Professor B., had apparently divorced himself entirely from my conception of medicine, for I received my notice immediately after completing my specialized training. I had particularly angered him in that

I had advised a patient that she could of course refuse a liver
puncture, which at that time could occasionally still be fatal,
since diagnosis alone is not the crown of medicine.

Meanwhile my wife and I finally had found a small situation.
A year later our oldest son was born. Psychotherapy here or
there, I had to earn money as soon as possible and finally found
suitable office space in the devastated city after a month-long
search. My parents helped me to bear the greater part of the
cost of setting up practice. Having thus established myself as an
internist, I was able to make a good start in spite of all the
difficult conditions.

Finally I could push forward in medicine, as I had always
understood it myself. I always saw the person of the patient and
his sickness; not until afterwards did I see the "case." It was
certainly unusual to work thus, but the patients were well aware
of it even though I often had to act quite impartially with them.
They valued and respected my way of thinking and so at the
same time provided further recommendations for patients. My
problem was always that of too much work, the loss of personal
medicine through the necessities of time in practice. Thus I
fought the battle against both sides: for my ideal and against
the routine of practice. In terms of my profession I stood alone
and could make my own decisions. However, I now had a large
family for which to care, where I was not alone. But in my
outlook on life and in the professional conduct of my practice,
I was and remained an oddity, a man for whom the insurance
companies made difficulties, since my record-keeping procedures
were not businesslike enough. In two proceedings before the
insurance companies, I had to convince my accusers of the opposite. I stood up for truth and justice in public life. I did not
use several insurance certificates in the same family in order
to give the impression that treatment would be cheaper if the cost
was distributed among more patients, and in this way also gained
their sympathy and recognition. For seventeen years I have
helped personal medicine to a new consideration, so far as it lay
in my power, but I have always stood fully alone.

Then, fortuitously, an invitation came one day from a good
acquaintance, the secretary of the academy, to go to Bad Boll
to attend a conference of the *médecine de la personne*. She was
of the opinion that this would apparently do something for me.

It was a small conference, with lectures by von Orelli, Theodore Bovet, Graf Lehndorff, and Bible study by Paul Tournier. When I heard him speak there, my heart began to beat wildly. There stood before me a man with similar experiences, very unpretentious, gracious, full of humor, but also dynamic, powerful, magnificent through the power of his faith, a prophet of his idea, and a man of the deepest religiosity. It was as if for the first time in my life I was seeing a real doctor, as he had been in my mind. This circle of colleagues appeared to be joined in a deep spirituality and friendship and in the utmost understanding of what that secret of love among men could do. It was as if I had been saved and freed from an authentic sorrow which I had carried around with me for so many years—my loneliness.

When I was asked to introduce myself, I said a few unimportant words. This was before Tournier's lecture. I did not yet know what was expected of me, that an introduction in this circle meant something different than an official businesslike attitude. My remarks must have appeared quite scanty therefore. When afterwards asked in a circle of all the participants what had influenced me the most, I was able to tell them something of what I had received: the internationality, the openness with which all the men there had mutually met and listened to each other, the true friendship, the lively union of spirituality and science in the psychological permeation of medicine and their therapeutic attitude toward the person. Paul Tournier turned around to me and asked his neighbor, "Qui est cet homme?" (Who is this man?) Then our glances met, and I had the clear feeling that he thought, "I know who you are."

For several years I have known now the place of my spiritual home among the doctors of this world. It is called *médecine de la personne,* the medicine of the whole person. I have found friends throughout the whole world and stand united with them. A great circle of brotherly minded men have gathered together thanks to Paul Tournier, the founder of this medicine of the whole person, to whom I offer the greatest admiration and honor, since he is the embodiment of what has always been the substance of my personal life. In all love, I do not feel myself dependent upon him, for he is a liberator who seeks no discipleship. He has always endeavored, on the contrary, to turn people away from putting all their attention on him and to encourage them to autonomous achievements. But for that very reason, my affection for him continues to grow, which is no fault of his but simply the result of his personal emanation and the love which he disseminates as an aura of shining humanitarianism. Perhaps he is therefore an authentic soul leader, a "guru" and master. I have followed him all the more dearly since he has gone the same way as I, full of solitude and resistance, yet proceeding in the greater expectation and experience of "you" and "we"—the way of friendship among all races, countries, and boundaries, and a doctor of medicine of the whole person.

KARL STOEVESANDT, M.D.

Internal Medicine
Bremen, West Germany

The Psychotherapeutic Scope of the Family Doctor

The Tournier conferences, the conferences of the medicine of the whole person at Bossey on beautiful Lake Geneva, are not just a distant image for my wife and me. They provide a stimulus and courage for the often tiring daily work in which the wife in a true marriage has a valid part even though she is not a specialist. In her husband's absence, she takes telephone messages, gives temporary short counsel, and is thereby particularly a doctor's wife and not only mother and housewife. When I write the following words about the doctor and the patient for the seventy-fifth birthday of our honored and beloved Paul Tournier, then my wife stands behind them and is glad to be a participant.

Over the past five decades there has been a constantly growing distinction between the clinician, the specialist, and the doctor in general practice. This may be regrettable, but it has become inevitable. The comparison of the possibilities among them is both necessary and desirable so that out of their differences will come no separation. It is apparent that all these groups have something essential to say to one another.

A specialty is justified where a special method is available for a particular area and is restricted to it. In marked measure that is the case with the family doctor. In order to speak plainly I

want to provide his specialty with a name: I call it the kitchen
and living room method. Psychology, testing, typology, analysis
—all this is not to be dispensed with as scientific explanation.
Far be it from me to detract from their value, or to belittle the
concern with them. But their exact application in the practice of
the family doctor not only creates difficulties; they are in many
regards unnecessary. The reasons are worth mentioning.

An individual glance into family life opens many things to me
which could not be answered through inquiries. A slightly ob-
scene picture in a secret place in the bedroom signifies something
of a dangerous situation with regard to eroticism. On the other
hand, a Christian calendar on the wall, a framed confirmation
decree over the bed point to the significance of the holding of a
tradition, which makes possible a counterclaim in the case of
difficult sickness, or health in a conflict situation.

And not only the small bookshelf or the beautifully polished
bookcase! The short moment of waiting should not be wasted
while the wife first unties her apron or while the servant, if there
is one, calls the woman. The observations are not normally noted
down into a patient's record no matter how well kept it is. It
would be valuable, but on the other hand, by wording it in
written form one too quickly presses into fixed judgment a picture which is yet to form. "Judge not, that ye be not judged."
This word from the Sermon on the Mount belongs in every place
where psychology is used, everywhere one man meets another,
everywhere the doctor encounters the patient. It is indeed not
so easy to decide whether disorder in the kitchen is carelessness,
whether it stems from an excess of need and care, or whether it
points to a chronic worry of the housewife. As there is a disorder
out of originality, so there is order out of sterile pedantry, and
also the making of order as the basis for concern with essential
things.

Is not this kitchen and living room method an enviable domain
of the family doctor? It saves much in careful or inquisitorial
inquiries, with people who in many cases are reserved and shy,
especially since the doctor must necessarily precede the beginning of the actual examination with them. And the method may
help set the cadence in which further questions are asked. How
helpless and forlorn I often feel in an appointment with a new
patient when I note deeply buried emotions; I know then I must

seek a fortuitous chance to look in on the household at a later time.

Once I was amazed when I visited a simple man who had made no particular impression on me during his appointment and found him in bed reading Kant's writing on eternal peace. When he asked whether or not I knew it, I was ashamed to have to answer no. I made up for the omission as soon as possible, for, like so many other books, it had stood unread on my bookshelf. On another occasion, I was surprised to see one of my women patients step from the waiting room into the consulting room still shoving a copy of Plato's *Dialogues* into her purse. The cause of her knowledge-seeking problem became clear to me later in her home.

I will not delay us with the portrayal of cases as they occur daily and are known by everyone. I will only say that the possibilities of the family doctor furnish clues which are not otherwise at hand. I must strongly emphasize, however, that the family doctor should let himself be stimulated through the success of strict psychotherapy to make real use of these clues to provide the leadership expected of him. Though we have been blinded by the glaring achievements of scientific medicine and forced through hypnotic pressure to use clinical procedures as much as possible, we realize they are not completely self-sufficient.

I may assimilate a novel with pleasure. I am still not the author, and am neither in the position of intervening in the outcome, nor am I called to do so. Are we not as doctors all too often mere readers and interested spectators in the real novels which play out under our eyes? We are involved in the drama not only as scene-shifters—namely, physically, mechanically, chemically—but also must very actively play a part on the stage. The old Curschmann in Leipzig used to mention that one should first examine a patient three times before speaking with him about the weather. That is both right and wrong. Adam Mueller, a philosopher in Vienna at the beginning of the nineteenth century, said that a right dialogue exists only if the dialogue partners stand under a common sky. Thus the simplest community of a spherical sky forms first of all a useful point of departure. In the home, which is a trusting atmosphere for a patient, the encounter is more easily guaranteed than in the strange space of the consulting room. Home visits are no expensive luxury, as insurance carriers many times suspect, but a useful means for the desired treatment. Though they may appear old-fashioned methodologically, the family doctor sees in them his advantage over the specialist and the hospital.

Yes, actually, they are life-epics of which we not only have a presentiment. Called biological anamnesis today, the case history is inquired into; it is opened to the family doctor as event. When he becomes old enough, he has been a long-time participant. He sees the generations, even including the great-grandchildren and the branch lines of the family in their breadth, and he experiences their friendship. I confess how fruitful, but indeed how unfortunate also, or how pleasurable—all of these—gossip from the same living quarters can be. The engagements, the breaking off of engagements, the illegitimate child, the first divorced man —these events fill the storehouse of anamnesis without the slightest violation of secrets. One must play the curious listener, so that the thread is not broken too quickly. Nevertheless, one hears not only the spicy in this way; through the report of a third person is revealed the patient's character—his readiness to help others, his skill in his occupation, his capability of judgment, his personality as a social being—all things which add to physical and psychosomatic understanding.

For as long as we continue to be thrown back to the piece-work of symptom-treatment—and the organ sickness under discussion is also, according to psychosomatic notions, only a symptom—the continuing commission of leadership in all life situations is given to the family doctor in a way almost unknown to his clientèle. What is mentioned independently of localized sickness can be only summarily and incompletely noted. The broad area of child education comes under discussion, from the preschooler with his intense activity in play to the pubescent child with his disturbing self-consciousness.

How is the family strengthened as the fundamental basis of social relations? Child education is at the same time parent education. The anxious mother must be taught not to breed into the child any neurosis. The father must let the son develop himself and painstakingly search out his vocational inclination. Difficulties in relation to school must be settled impartially.

Where is sickness the result of external natural causes, and where must one presume that sickness represents flight? Ulcers and asthma, spastic digestive disturbances, and menstruation disturbances many times point to an inner conflict. But is that always the case? Is it right to find out about it instead of leaving the person time to take care of it himself, even where the family doctor perceives the situation? He is indeed constrained in the surroundings to proceed with discretion in his field of vision. Thus can and must he constantly lead the conversation around to the subject of life-relationships, irritations over fellow-lodgers, the employer, or the marriage partner. He will often not be able to take any action, but he may not, with the words, "That's none of my business," avoid the role of the catalyst for the working out of decisions.

He must make a considered decision whether the appointment hour is more favorable for productive dialogue than the easier though random situation in the home. I have had the experience, for example, that the minutes spent in preparing for x-rays may loosen the patient's tongue somewhat toward answering questions about sexual relations. The patient does not need to turn his glance aside ashamedly, just as in general during the technical investigation—taking a blood sample or determining a blood count—the patient can be led to fill out the gaps in his case history. The medical technician then, instead of being a help, is a hindrance, as the time which is used by the doctor for such technical activity is by no means lost. One can almost best express it that medical activity is in danger of solidifying itself. It is much more in accord with its function that it should remain focused entirely on the person.

Conduct, treatment, diagnosis are interwoven with each other. Indeed, diagnosis is no simple, logical act run off according to a kind of analysis of the physical chemical process. The possibility for empathy is in reality a weighty factor. Diagnosis is a "seeing through," an "understanding"; not an "establishing" or a "determination by analysis" as the people and the dictionary like to translate it. It is an old hobby horse that I ride here. I explicitly forbid on medical certificates, or in connection with the bill for private insurance, that anything more be taken from my diagnoses than that this man is sick, or was sick, and therefore has a justifiable claim for medical help. A numbered rubrics table is sufficient for determining who must pay and how much; or the table could serve as a public statistical basis for a world improvement that is desired but not yet actively under attack.

Diagnosis is subjective interpretation. It is objective only insofar as limited probability represents it as certainty. Through the
body we push the psyche, or the other way around. The mystery
or the wonder, "man," the creation of God, grown from molecu-
lar chromosomes and formed through the environment, shows
himself to us as a representation, indeed a portrait, never the
object itself. Therefore the diagnosis is never finished, but must
actually always remain in change and in a state of becoming.

A further remark is in order here. In the words like *diagnosis*
and *epic crisis* is mirrored the noble language power of the
Greeks, who knew how to give their insights descriptive names.
If I am a follower of this rich humanistic background, which is
the doctor's also, then this is reason enough to return again to
the original sense of our traditional terminology. With several
diseases like measles and scarlet fever, which apparently run a
typical course, the name is sufficient description in spite of the
variations in individual cases. But one thinks of the report of
Thucydides about the so-called plague in the Peloponnesian
War. He gives an ongoing description of the symptoms in almost
our present-day textbook language, although without the trouble
of textbook names. He says he has made a detailed inquiry into
it, and he adds, concisely and conclusively, "Also I have gone
through it myself." The description is so good that we can be
certain the disease was treated as typhus.

We point out to the family doctor the possibility which is his
especially, and therefore his obligation, of careful anamnesis
which is due the clinic. He stands at the flow of events where
in the fusion of body and psyche, obligations for human life
are imposed upon him. That is his burden and his honor. Indeed,
it leads to a compassion that is something more than compassion,
for compassion is often nothing more than a passing emotion.

This is the duty of therapy—in German, of *dienens*, "serving";
in Latin, of *curans*, "caring". Through long use *cura*, the word
"care", has been worn down to "heal" (*heilen* in German), as if
we were the ones who could heal. We can, through our service,
only be helpful: "Natura sanat, medicus curat." Therefore we
are modest, with no unduly great trust in our deeds, but thankful
for the mandate of the attempt to heal.

Finally, a word also needs to be said about death as the

terminal limit of medical care. Death, as the mandate for ministerial care, nevertheless often enters before the pastor. This care of souls must many times be taken to the relatives. It is the doctor who makes space and time real for those closest to the departed, and he will do this service better the more he reminds himself that "in the midst of life, we are surrounded by death." In the unanimity of sorrow, the family doctor, not as a blind factor, but as a Christian, has come under the sign of the cross, which in the West in a paradoxical way is a symbol of life.

RICHARD EEG-OLOFSSON, M.D.

Psychiatrist
Stockholm, Sweden

Attitude to Life, to One's Fellow-Man, and Health: Some Reflections

It may be considered self-evident that a doctor's attitude to life and to his fellow-man, and the values this attitude embraces and is based upon, should in some way find expression in his own daily life. With the phrase "in some way" I wish to indicate that this expression need not be in direct formulations, but rather in his comportment, in his way of meeting his patients. But situations do arise where one must declare one's view of what should inform and leaven a person's conduct. I was made particularly aware of this at an early stage in my work when a patient with domestic problems and concomitant psychosomatic symptoms suddenly blurted: "But that's living as a fine art!" Well, and so it was, indeed. We were discussing how one tries rightly to cope with the suspicion and the misinterpretations of the critical people in one's ambience.

In a way, perhaps the psychotherapist is forced most of all to work with the problems entailing valuations.[1] But in our pluralistic community no practicing physician escapes the confrontation with conflicts affecting the lives and health of human beings. We need only to call to mind the transplantation of organs, measures designed to prolong life in "hopeless cases," contraceptives for minors, abortions, thoughtless separations.

But the researchers, too, are faced with important decisions in which ethical points of view may be decisive. This is illustrated by The Helsinki Declaration, the directive that was adopted in

June 1964 by the World Medical Association in Helsinki for physicians engaged in clinical experimental research. This I regard as an expression for the spirit of humility that is shared by science and religion and acknowledges both the dignity and rights of the individual. Ernst Kretschmer is worth quoting in this connection. "The scientist's picture of the world is closely akin to the religious picture, for in both cases there springs from the astonished wonder by which we are seized when confronted by things that are greater and mightier than we and by their ineluctable laws the feeling of an 'absolute dependence' that Schleiermacher designates as the basic religious emotion."

One can even muster some understanding for one who in the face of man's often inhuman behavior represents him as *only* an animal among animals. Nevertheless, one is still unpleasantly touched when in our mass media this view is put forward as something self-evident. And not only there. In an ambitious periodical distributed to the doctors of Sweden one finds the sentence: "But as in the case of other animals also man's maximal life-duration is genetically determined or programmed." [2] Would it not have been more adequate to speak of man as a being among other living beings? If people are determined to see man as an animal then there is not much reason to be surprised that he is also treated as such. *Vestigia terrent!* Certainly one finds such tendencies not only in Sweden. It is the little word *only* that makes the statement fundamentally false. If the animal is fettered by its nature in the reality in which it lives, incalculable possibilities hover over man's reality. "Man alone can seek and proclaim the truth. . . . It is this that makes man the great exception in Nature—something completely unique in the chain of development. . . . It is this that in the last analysis saves us from total misanthropy. . . ." The quotation is from a recently published essay entitled "The open hand and the closed" by one of Sweden's finest essayists, Hans Ruin. But I think this train of thought is shared by many. Is it not a task for medicine of the person to remind people again and again that man represents a qualitative leap in evolution, that he is much more than *only* an animal?

But let us return to the practicing physician, whether specialist or general practitioner. Apart from the above-mentioned more special questions, it may prove necessary to be furnished with a

more thoroughly thought-out view of man and of life if one is
to be able to discuss different attitudes that cause sickness either
in the one holding them or in those in his ambience or in both.
One must also be able humbly to acknowledge that health is
not the highest value, and that it is, accordingly, not the ultimate
criterion of the rightness of an attitude to life. In *Cancer Ward*
Alexander Solzhenitsyn gives expression to these trains of
thought when he lets one of the characters in the book exclaim:
". . . . And from this you draw the logical conclusion that I came
to you to get saved *at all costs*. But I do not want that, not at all
costs! There's nothing in this world that I'd be willing to pay
any price at all for." But perhaps for that which is not of this
world, one would like to add.

As regards suffering as such, one meets with different attitudes.
Some people refuse to accept it; others accept it all too readily.
The question of anodynes and sedatives enters here.

In this connection I will mention an institution in Sweden
known as the St. Luke Foundation. In a very short space of time
it has grown enormously. The first paragraph of its statutes runs
as follows:

"The St. Luke Foundation is an association of ministers,
doctors, social workers and others engaged or interested in
ministrations to those in need. The Foundation bases its activities
on a Christian view of man, with particular emphasis on cor-
porate life and mutuality in human relations. The Foundation
sees it as its chief task to promote the care and treatment of sick
persons whose impaired health is due to unsolved inner conflicts
or alienation from their fellows. Also in other respects the
Foundation wants to counteract and treat domestic discord and
disturbances in personality. In these contexts the Foundation
represents an integrated view of man which acknowledges the
importance for human health of people's attitude to life and the
values they espouse."

It seems to me that a mention of the foundation is in place in
a volume of homage to Paul Tournier.

When the foundation was formed thirty years ago, one of the
prime movers, the authoress Ebba Pauli, wrote a book entitled
Struggle or Resignation. She gave it as her opinion that far too
often Christians became resigned, took up a passive attitude to
sickness and suffering with the motivation that they were sent

by God. Thus it was from the very outset realized by the St. Luke Foundation that it ought to represent an attitude to life having an active struggle against sickness and suffering on its program.

The approach is by no means lacking in topicality even today. I do, certainly, think that the general attitude has changed in the direction of increased militancy. And I think that more than formerly we understand the prophet Jeremiah where he says: "Righteous art thou, O Lord, when I plead with thee: yet let me talk with thee of thy judgments" (Jer. 12:1). But in our Swedish hymnal we still find this verse: "How should I not gladly meet my torment? It is an angel, sent from my God. How should I ask the good Father why he chose it as his messenger?"

To find instances of the connection between our attitude to life and our health one may take examples from different fields. One may here find the whole psychosomatic panorama displayed. When one is brought face to face with pressing and pressed human beings one often wonders what happened to the blessings of our prosperity. There is a connection between stress and cardiac infarction. Cigarette smoking is harmful. But is not the stress a contributory cause of immoderate smoking that functions like whiplashes whereby a *circulosus vitiosus* arises? [3] However, I will content myself with three examples taken from my daily experience. I use them with the consent of the persons in question.

The first is taken from my work in the St. Luke Foundation and refers to a woman, aged fifty, who had fallen into a state of insufficiency of depressive type. She had previously consulted a doctor but had been unwilling to inform him of an important cause, as she did not want to expose her husband, who was such "a fine and upright man." As a matter of fact, however, she lived under constant pressure, as he was constantly criticizing everything she said and did. In the contact I had with him, he at first affected total incomprehension of the role he played in his wife's difficulties. There was so much that he *had* to criticize. She might, for the rest, be grateful to be married to a man like himself, a non-smoker who did not drink and had never been unfaithful.

In this case, a person's attitude to life and to his fellows, or lack of any attitude, led above all to suffering for others. The only course open to the physician was to enter the family situation as a fellow human being, for inevitably the children also were drawn into the conflicts, hidden or not. This was, in other words, a therapy of the type which has since been more systematically developed under the name of family therapy, a therapy in which the therapist's values neither can nor are to be concealed. But this, of course, does not mean forcing one's views on another.

My second example differs as little as the foregoing from what we meet with practically every day. A good many years ago a middle-aged man was referred to me. He had sought medical advice chiefly for intestinal trouble that had been diagnosed as "nervous." As the sequel was to show, his symptoms followed psychodynamic laws, for the fact of the matter was that what most. troubled him was not his intestines but the circumstance that things did not go smoothly at his place of work. He felt that he was misunderstood by others, thought that the younger people did not show him sufficient respect, and that they joked with him in a way he did not like. It soon became clear even to him that the "fault" was to be sought for not only in those around him. He had—as he himself expressed it—a demanding attitude to people and a privilege-complex in his relations with them. This was in itself easy to understand when one heard him speak of his difficulties as a child and as an unemployed person during the depression in Sweden in the 1930s. But he was unreconciled with his existence, and this led to illness. Obviously, medicine was here of no avail; what was needed was a changed attitude to life. As this gradually came about, his problems of coopera-tion and therewith his impaired health little by little subsided. His justified reaction to the injustice he met with was now no longer directed against those in his surroundings or against people who had done him no wrong. He no longer took what had happened as a personal insult. But there remained a claim on himself to help, to the best of his ability, the endeavors to change the community for the better. With this disappeared his aggressiveness, which had earlier led him to be unnecessarily (and consciously) provoking.

I do not for a moment mean that one must accept life with its injustice just as it is. But one must reconcile oneself to the fact that one may meet with great disappointments, severe trials, suffering, and unhappiness. The word *reconciliation* gives another and deeper perspective than acceptance. To be reconciled with suffering means to struggle on with spiritual buoyancy in spite of all. To be content with only accepting implies a much lesser engagement, a resignation. When one is reconciled, one can meet the difficulties of life without bitterness and use one's forces to improve what can be improved. In the spirit of acceptation one may shrug one's shoulders at the vanity of all things in the feeling that one's contribution signifies nothing. For me at least there is a great difference between these two attitudes.

My third example deals with false feelings of guilt and touches upon the connection between medical and religious ministrations on the spiritual plane.

A thirty-seven-year-old woman had problems of a kind that lend themselves readily to generalization. She considered herself on the whole to have been like most of her fellows, perhaps somewhat more unsure of herself than the majority of people. She wanted to be a Christian, but she had sometimes doubted whether she stood in a right relation to God. (It may be observed in parenthesis to the many who find themselves in a similar situation that one must be able to rely on oneself if one is not to live in perpetual anxiety that one is not relying on God in the right way.)

Her mother had died a couple of years earlier, and in this connection she began to experience uneasiness and anxiety she had formerly not felt. She lost her gaiety and became more and more unsure of herself. It was, in other words, a not unusual reaction to grief. In her sorrow she turned to her minister. From what he had said and not said, the following had become etched in her mind: "You have not prayed perseveringly enough." (This is a cliché I have often met with.) She fell into despair and began to pray and read the Bible constantly, so that finally she had to be hospitalized in a state of confusion. Here she was given an *in et per se* perfectly correct medical treatment but not, on the other hand, any help with her religious problems. After a short time she could be discharged from the hospital, but feelings of unworthiness, restlessness, and disturbed sleep persisted. She had also become afraid of meeting other people. It was in this situation that she came to consult me.

To be content, in a case like this, with purely medical prescriptions would have been wrong. Accordingly, she was persuaded to make contact with the St. Luke Foundation. When I saw her again about a year later, she was in good mental balance but needed help with a troublesome fatigue that was then considered to be satisfactorily explained by anemia. But she still found it difficult to get away from the disapproving phrase cited in the foregoing.

In conclusion I will touch very briefly on two points. The one is that it is scarcely necessary to point out that our attitude to life and to our fellows has a connection both with our picture of the world and our *Weltanschauung*. But a common view of life does not necessarily imply a sharing of our attitude to life and to our fellow-man. One can have a Christian view of or understanding of life, but the attitude to life may differ: it may be life-denying and ascetic in the one and life-affirming and freer in the other. There will then be a varying attitude to sexuality, aggression, self-realization, and self-sacrifice, to take only a few examples, from individual to individual, from milieu to milieu.

One of our Swedish poets, Lars Englund, with whom I came into contact, coined the phrase *evangelical light-heartedness,* in his wonderment that Christ, who knew more about evil than any other, should nevertheless teach us to consider the lilies of the field and the birds of the air. In the way that poets have, Englund was giving expression in a new and living way to an old, frequently forgotten truth.

It may further be pointed out that there is a connection between a person's view of life and his health also in the sense that health affects the view of life. It may probably be safely assumed that one who has always good health will not view life and his fellows with the same eyes as one who has always been sickly. This is something that plays a great role in Adler's individual psychology. Lord Byron's club foot is often taken as an example of the correctness of this psychology. On his death-bed he gave instructions that he should be laid out in such a way that the club foot should as far as possible be concealed.

Dear Paul Tournier! We in Sweden have much to thank you for. In the first place you have visited us personally, in the second place your books have been translated into our language.

This little essay is quite in line with your way of thinking. Let it be a voice in the choir. Choir song has its given place, however good the soloists may be.

Notes

1. Cf. Charlotte Buhler, *Values in Psychotherapy* (New York: Free Press, 1962), Jules H. Masserman, ed., *Psychoanalysis and Human Values* (New York: Grune & Stratton, Inc., 1960), and A. Maslow, ed., *New Knowledge in Human Values* (New York: Harper & Row, 1959).
2. *Recip Reflex*, October 1970.
3. See *Proceedings of the VIIth International Congress of Psychotherapy*, Part III.

ARTHUR JORES, M.D.

Professor of Internal Medicine and
Director of the Clinic of the University of Hamburg
Former Rector of the University of Hamburg
Hamburg, West Germany

The Dialogical Relationship between the Doctor and the Patient in a Medicine of the Whole Person

No dialogical relationship exists in contemporary medicine between the doctor and patient. In the first encounter the past history is "taken." After the patient's first sentences the doctor is already forming an image in his mind as to which sickness could be at hand. Thus the statements of the patient are quickly cut short by the doctor. On his part he begins to ask questions in order to confirm further the impression in his mind as to which sickness it could be. In doing so it is not unusual for symptoms and troubles which do not occur in this picture to be ignored and the true events obscured. This conversation can directly affect the character of an investigation. The doctor is the knowledgeable one, the patient the ignorant one, who has only to answer the questions.

After the collection of the prehistory, the examination follows in which the patient also is not informed as to why this or that examination is being carried through. The diagnosis which the doctor makes is scarcely imparted to the patient. He receives a prescription on which in most cases today several medications are designated. This too is handed over to him without any explanation. Frequently prescriptions are given for the patient's behavior which can severely limit his life style. Since many doctors are of the opinion that all sicknesses in the world come from smoking and drinking, both are almost always forbidden. The doctor thus issues authoritative orders and expects the patient to obey.

This situation is particularly obvious in the hospital. There are three hierarchies firmly structured in themselves, but which naturally also communicate with one another: the doctoral, the nursing, and the administrative. Although the claim is always made that everything in the hospital takes place for the well-being of the patient, it is often in actuality the case that the patient is there for the sake of these three hierarchies and is handed over to them. During the diagnostic phase everything happens without the patient's previously being oriented as to what examinations are being made. Other than the taking of the prehistory, a conversation with the doctors seldom takes place. In addition, the diagnosis is usually not given to the patient. He must then swallow a great number of variously colored tablets, of whose purpose and function he also is ignorant. He is then released with the information, "When you see your doctor again he will have a report." In the report, the results of a great number of examinations, mostly normal, are presented, and in the end suggestions are given which are only of slight use for the doctor. Only his conscience is pacified. Everything that can be done has now been done so that nothing serious is overlooked.

The picture painted above may in many respects be overdrawn, but basically it is true. It points to the fact that even if the doctor is friendly, there is nevertheless a gulf existing between him and the patient—created by the fact that the doctor's knowledge is basically inexplicable to the other and consequently has to be obeyed. Doctors distinguish between pleasant and unpleasant patients. The pleasant patient is the one who is quiet and without contradiction follows faithfully all orders of the doctor. The unpleasant patient asks questions. He shows he has heard something about this or that medical theme, or has seen it on television, and he is critical of therapy and asks whether this or that medication might not be better for him. Unfortunately there are doctors who react very sharply and aggressively to such questions.

Something basically new came into the doctor-patient relationship by means of psychotherapy. Freud taught us that one experiences more if one does not question but only listens with "suspended watchfulness." This fully unprejudiced type of listening opens entirely new aspects to the doctor and creates an entirely different atmosphere of reciprocal relationships, especially if he also links the conversation to the life-situation of the patient. Of course, Freudian analysis, with its extensive passivity of the therapist, the holding up of the mirror, and the only occasional interpretations, is also not quite dialogical. The personal engagement of the therapist is lacking. Now and then patients have come to me who had finally broken off orthodox analysis since they had been so frustrated through this missing engagement of the doctor that they could not stand it any longer. The psychotherapist Görres, in a critical report of Freudian analysis, has spoken very accurately of the aseptical operating theater in which this treatment takes place. In the meantime many types of changes in psychotherapy have taken place which have turned this into a dialogical relationship even though certain orthodox analysts defend their position as before.

When, decades ago, Paul Tournier began a medicine of the whole person, he intended exactly this: that the doctor would encounter the patient as a person in his entirety and meet him thus as a person face to face, even though it is a case of an unknowing one coming to a knowing one. We want to consider this relationship somewhat more closely and establish what basic conditions must be fulfilled. The first of these is the above-mentioned capacity for being able to listen with complete freedom and openness to the other, observing everything that he says, as in the following example:

> An approximately forty-year-old patient came to me complaining of heart trouble. After hearing her description of the problem, it was evident to me that it should be treated as nervous trouble rather than organic. I tried to find out about her life situation and to assure myself that everything was in the best order. When I found that it was not, I asked her if she would think again as to whether or not there were problems in her life. She looked out the window and said, "Indeed, in the highest degree—my daughter is also about to marry a man who is much older than she."

Here one must be aware of the little word *also*. Here lay the true problem of her individual life situation, one with which she was still not finished.

This treatment of the doctor presupposes that he is free of all affective reactions and moralistic values. Sentimentally affective impulses, however, do occur in us, and it is important to recognize this. Balint once said that the feeling which moves the patient must be produced in the doctor. Thus the introspection of the doctor is important, and just as important as veracity. Veracity is not identical with truth. A man is truthful who behaves according to his nature. Untruthfulness is the same as hypocrisy.

A further condition is the patience and the preparation of the doctor, even to questioning himself and admitting error. It is of critical significance for the patient to feel himself accepted and understood by his doctor. What is called acceptance here is affirming the other as he is; understanding is taking the trouble to sympathize with the actual manner of relating of the other. This, however, is the position of love.

Seguin, a psychotherapist living in Mexico, has written a little book, *The Doctor and His Patient,* which was translated into German at the instigation of Boss. Here Seguin undertakes a critique of Freud's concept of transference and is of the opinion that it is much too anemic. A particular form of love relationship must exist between the doctor and patient, but one which is basically different from all other types of love relationships such as exist between parents and children, between two friends, between teacher and student, or between different sexes. Seguin speaks of psychotherapeutic *eros* as a love relationship between two men who admit no superiority or inferiority. Both encounter themselves in the sense of Tournier as whole persons.

It has often been discussed as to what actually helps in psychotherapy. It has always been clear that it is not the analytical explanations of depth psychological associations, but only what Freud called transference. That is, however, much less than the concept of psychotherapeutic *eros,* for the transference belongs again in the aseptic operating room. After sufficient experience in psychotherapy, I know that if such psychotherapeutic *eros* actually exists between the doctor and the patient, the interval required for such therapy is much less than that of classical, analytical therapy.

It would, however, certainly be wrong to make use of this doctor-patient relationship only for the psychotherapeutic situation. It is also possible in the scientific medicine about which we spoke in the beginning of this essay, and it can be of decisive significance for therapeutic results in it. For the patient's understanding, the doctor would need to give him suitable information concerning the necessity of diagnostic examinations, diagnosis, and the type of treatment. At this point the question of truth emerges, particularly if it is a matter of serious illness, perhaps a carcinoma. Truth requires its hour. I can damage an unprepared patient twofold with truth. In the doctor-patient relationship described here, truth is possible if it is at the right time. Authority as such is not eliminated, but it is based not on office and not on rank, but on greater knowledge and on individual personal structure. But only the doctor who works on himself constantly and has experienced his own maturity can function in this sense. There is no doubt that a didactical analysis can be a great help here. In C. G. Jung's words: "Every doctor can lead his patient only so far as he himself is."

For all those who actually know Paul Tournier and have read his books, there is nothing new in my remarks. He has represented personal medicine for us all in the sense described above and has always shown us that the co-human relationship described here is the relationship which Christ has taught us and set before us as an example.

KARLFRIED GRAF DÜRCKHEIM, PH.D.

Professor, Psychotherapist
Todtmoos/Schwarzwald, West Germany

Medicine of the Whole Person for Unbelieving Patients

Man is a healthy, whole man only if he has become a person or is on the way to letting his fundamentally always personal nature actually become a person. Man becomes a person in the full sense of the word only to the extent that the absolute core of his nature, beyond space and time and always individual, sounds through his space-time limited life-form ("personare"), so that he knows he is determined in his existence by this individual presence of the divine in him and is committed to it.

It is entirely the same whether a man is physically sick or healthy, whether he suffers psychologically or not. He is "unhealthy" as a person if the indwelling, transcendent depth of nature in him is not resonant, that is, his essence is not integrated. It is quite the same whether one is physically or psychically healthy or suffering: he is still healthy as a person to the extent that the unconditional core of his nature sounds throughout his personality, which is conditioned and affected by the world, and—often just *in* his sorrow—is on the way to being integrated.

The doctor who intends man to be a person is consciously or unconsciously drawn in his diagnosis and his therapy to this person-becoming, that is, he strives for transparence for the transcendence which is always indwelling in man. He knows that ultimately only from that come the healing powers, the powers which correspond to the actual determination of man and therewith also to his becoming whole.

How the person of a patient can be spoken to depends on where the doctor and patient stand religiously. If the patient is quite active in his Christian faith, then the doctor, if he himself is a believing Christian, can bring any situation of sickness into a fruitful relation to the life and death of Christ. And he can do this in such a way that not only does he further the convalescence of the sickness at the time, but he helps the patient on his way to greater personal maturity.

The believing Christian who confesses and practices his faith is becoming less obvious in our time. One always finds himself dealing with men who have turned their backs on the church and no longer even want to be confronted with God and Christ. That does not mean, however, that these "unbelievers" could not nevertheless be religious, and, indeed, religious in the knowledge of a transcendence immanent to them and their world. Then it is critical for the doctor, whether he personally stands in a confession of faith or not, to be conscious of the divine core of his nature and to draw out that essence in others. The possibility of touching upon this core in others grows to the same extent that the doctor knows about a basic religious experience.

There can be no doubt that there are in principle basic experiences that are possible, accessible to, and meant for all people about that which precedes all being. This is the prerequisite and root of all religions, and without it religion cannot live. "Were the eye not sensitive to the sun, the eye would not recognize it." That there is this primitive experience, and that two men can encounter themselves in it or in retrospect, is the actual presupposition of a full medicine of the whole person.

In the religious basic experience, man is touched by all the space and time conditions given to this world, which encompass and keep life in constant change—to which either stopping or hardening is opposed. This obduracy happens not only in the interpretation of the basic experience in religion but also in man in general, through his inherent and objectively established consciousness which distinguishes him from animal, and through his ego which longs for a secure position in the world. In the hardening of his regimen, the union with the original source is always narrower and finally interrupted.

The possibility of convalescence from any sickness depends upon overcoming the rigidity so that the changing and thereby healing life can again flow in. The right doctor is always thereby directed to melt away firmly developing façades, attitudes, customs, conceptions, be they of a general type or specially drawn to the acute situation.

The psychology of our time has confirmed without doubt that the inhibition of a transcendent function, that is to say, the hindering of the developing conscience and the capacity for living of the transcendent core, is just as often the cause for psychological and, accordingly, physical sorrows also, as is the oppression of "natural impulses." The doctor who has the person in view can always proceed from the position that even in an emphatically unbelieving, i.e., religiously impenitent, patient, the actual healing powers still lie dormant, but can be freed where he succeeds in creating an entrance into the depth of his patient's nature. This is particularly impeded only where a vehement opposition to a rigid "religion" has made a man allergic to everything that has somehow to do with "religion." There are nevertheless many "unbelievers" who are genuinely endowed with qualities in which the divine touches the human. They are sensitive to everything numinous and sacral but are ashamed to confess it to others, since it could appear as if they were again embracing "religion," or because it reminds them of the "holy aspect" of the church.

Experience teaches that it is possible to melt the resistance in these men and to reawaken in them a healing spirit of great potential. What are the prerequisites?

For the doctor directed to the person, the first is, and naturally remains, that he also earn trust as a specialist in classical medicine.

The second is that the doctor experience the other as a *thou,* and show a warm, feeling heart to the man who is suffering under his actual situation. It is, however, critical for healing in the spirit of medicine of the whole person that the doctor not get stuck on the plane of human sympathy.

The third presupposition is therefore that he dare to step out of the plane of the ego which is suffering under the world and life and into the realm of the transcendent nature, which is the unconditional and otherworldly nature. But how does one open the eyes of the unbeliever?

Experience teaches that it is possible if the unbeliever is

successful in remembering numinous experiences and then lets himself earnestly embrace those which till now he has neglected or denied. The presupposition is only that the doctor himself know such experiences.

There is the experience of the *feeling of being*. In those moments man feels himself unexpectedly touched by the numinous. There is an unmistakable quality which has little to do with ordinary feeling, and, indeed, exceeds the most beautiful of feelings. Beyond that, into this quality the pleasant and the unpleasant combine fascination and mystery—*tremendum*, "a making happy with a deep wonder or fear"; for the encounter with transcendence always signifies at the same time a liberation from the narrowness of the ordinary consciousness of reality and therewith the withering of the ordinary ego. The painful prospering, the sorrowful enrapturing of this experience occurs to man at the easiest place where he is able to surrender his ego: in the vastness of nature, in the encounter with authentic art, in eroticism, in love, in the preparation to die. There is scarcely a man in great sorrow, who, appealed to in the right way, does not remember such moments. Here then is the possibility to appeal to the indwelling essence in the partner. Through the remembrance of numinous experiences he may be released from the convulsions of the obdurate ego demands and human suffering which make him sick and block his convalescence.

We can make contact through the otherworldly being which is present in our nature—in unbelievers no less than in others—in the so-called "Great Experiences of Being." Here are treated experiences in the boundary situation, of which, basically speaking, there are three: the imminence of *death*, the encounter with the *absurd*, and radical *solitude*. Anxiety before death, hopelessness in the absurd, and despair of solitude are three fundamental human miseries whose experience can bring a man to the limit of his life's ability.

There is the situation—not through man, but grace—that at the boundary of extinction the possibility is offered to man to do something which he could never do as an ordinary ego: to accept threatening death! Where it quite suddenly happens that in the moment of greatest anxiety the ego frees the space for what it has been denying, in a flash the otherworldly being can flow in and be experienced overpoweringly as life which is beyond life and death and thus not able to be reached by this death. Man experiences then a sudden change from an existence in an always-threatened and anxious ego to life of a nature which has become rooted in indestructible being.

Similar experiences are possible where it is allowed to man to accept in his extreme distress the absurdity of a situation or its solitude; it may then happen to him that he experiences the otherworldly and opposite existence as sense beyond sense and nonsense, as love beyond love and hate.

More men than we know today—unbelievers no less than others—carry such an experience deep in their hearts. Often at the time they did not feel entirely comfortable. Thus it is possible not only to call these experiences into memory but to let their memory bring about a change.

A "great experience of being" is the secret and wholly recognized treasure in many "unbelievers." Again and again serious illness not only calls such experience out of the forgotten but allows it for the first time to become a fruitful healing and renewing power.

The knowledge of the experience of being and feeling of being, that is, the several ways the divine being touches and calls us in particular experiences, is of great importance for the doctor who seeks the person in illness. To the extent that he himself is pervaded by otherworldly life he can let it resound as changing and healing power in others, be it in the middle of the appointment or afterward. Paul Tournier is model and master at producing this effect.

Sooner or later every doctor has to do with believing or unbelieving patients, some of whom stand firmly in their faith and some of whom have lost their faith or perhaps have never had any. In contact with "unbelieving" patients and students, with those who are distressed and those who are seeking counsel, I have come to several useful realizations for the doctor who relates not only to their sickness but also to their persons. In these judgments I feel myself in a particular way bound to Paul Tournier even though we may speak a different language now and then.

Paul Tournier has helped innumerable men, not only as doctor to patient, but as man to man, as I to thou, as person to person. Paul Tournier was able to do that in his way only because the presence of God prevailing within him, bearing and saving him, enables him in his divine core to speak to and call as a whole man to his fellow-man, but without necessarily speaking of God. But he was able also to listen to men who otherwise could not hear the word of God, speaking of God to them so that they saw and felt a spark of the spirit which is beyond all pictures and words. And as it sprang up and began to burn within them, their hearts were warmed and for the first time an authentic healing process could begin to work.

Left: *Sorrento, Italy, 1972*

Below: *With Paul Plattner, on the Rhine, 1972*

Above: *Pont à Mousson, France, 1972*

Right: *Portugal, 1971*

ERNEST IRRMANN, M.D.

Surgeon
Strasbourg, France

Medicine of the Whole Person and Psychosomatic Medicine

The concept of psychosomatic medicine has become an every-day part of medical practice; even the term "the person" is used currently in the publications concerning it by the most authoritative names in official medicine. To propagate today a medicine of the whole person would seem then to be forcing doors that are already open.

Paul Tournier's first book, which appeared in Geneva in 1940 under this title, gives him a right to having invented it; but who remembers? Nor does anyone wonder what it meant to those who used it first and what meaning it has for its actual adherents.

The psychological shock produced by this book led several doctors preoccupied with the human problems induced by illness to meet for the first time August 24–31, 1947, at the Chateau de Bossey in Vaud Canton, seat of the Ecumenical Council of Churches. The Bossey weeks were thereafter organized from year to year, also in other places and other countries, with a wider international representation. How to explain the persistence of this movement when the demands which had justified its beginnings seem to have been satisfied by the rise of psychosomatic medicine? Could there be something which causes it to differ from the latter, which gives it a distinctive character, an originality sufficient to explain its survival?

The medicine of the whole person, as practiced by Paul Tournier, was sure to meet serious resistance, along with its enthusiastic reception by some, because of its religious inspiration. Indeed, it came out of the Oxford Movement, very fashionable before the last World War in certain Protestant circles, and Paul Tournier's book was actually dedicated to the founder of the Oxford Group, Dr. Frank Buchman. I remember that after the war, in the discussion which followed a lecture by the author at the medical school at Strasbourg, a professor of biology, actually a very erudite and broad-minded person, reproached the lecturer severely for mixing up medicine, a science in the process of becoming more and more exact, with normal disciplines, not confined to facts, in order to formulate moral rules. Since the medicine of the whole person includes the acceptance of religion, it can be reproached with its irrational and antiscientific character. Practically speaking, it can be irritating that the daily schedule of the work sessions of the group includes, like those of the Oxford Group, silent morning meditations on biblical texts; it is possible not to agree with the biblical studies of Paul Tournier and reproach them with theological dilettantism. It is easy to see that what for some is a major attraction, for others is repugnant.

At least one cannot say that Paul Tournier did not display his colors from the beginning. Later, without denying the biblical inspiration of his action, he was to emphasize more and more the universal character of the medicine of the whole person, without distinction between religious persuasion or philosophical conviction. The practice of this medicine should suit the believer as well as the agnostic and should be applied to patients who are nonbelievers as well as to believers. This broadening beyond the frontiers of established religious practice has without doubt alienated a certain number of followers from the movement over the years, but in exchange has brought the sympathetic adherence of others.

What in this new approach to the medicine of the whole person renders it distinct from psychosomatic medicine as it is generally practiced? Does it not risk dissolution in giving up its initial support? Does it retain a specific, an irreplaceable character of its own?

As far as somatic and psychological factors are concerned, nothing distinguishes the medicine of the whole person from psychosomatic medicine. Both place essential value on the life story of the patient, on race, nationality, family, religion, profession, environment and, in short, on all his biological and psychological past and on the conflicts resulting from it. From birth to death, the human life develops along a horizontal line which is the history of each individual, and each theoretical pinpoint along this line is the event that situates him between the known past and the past buried in the subconscious and the unconscious, and the totally unknown future. He becomes conscious of the event through his self, which needs solid organic support. The storage of the past in his memory provides continuity in the retrospective vision of the lived. To a materialistic and organicist science, this self represents the result of the burden of memories of lived happenings during the existence of the individual concerned. The neuro-endocrinological balance of the organism at the moment and the way in which it accepts the present and the sum of experience and memories either conscious or made conscious by psychoanalytic techniques make an individual healthy or ill.

It is obvious that in this view of things the human being, in his physical and psychic dimensions, is reduced to little more than a functional arrangement of amino acids which through tens of millennia have grouped themselves by chance in the course of evolution and by progressive complexification have ended up at the stage where we now find ourselves, as Jacques Monod put it in *Chance and Necessity*. There can be no question of free choice, for choice is a function of a rigorous biological, psychological and sociological determinism, therefore an ineluctable necessity.

Not everyone agrees with this view of things. Jean Delay, one of the leaders of the French psychosomatic school, recognizes that in the human being there exists something which cannot be explained by the law of causality. The experience of many individuals who have lived through imminent danger of death have learned that a central core of their being remained independent of events and left them serene in the face of the tragic destiny toward which they were surely moving. This detachment from the support of the psycho-organic can be obtained through appropriate training, such as the oriental disciplines, like the Vedanta and Zen Buddhism. A science which is striving for objectivity should take notice of these realities.

That part of the person thus revealed is no longer the self that is bogged down in the futilities of daily living, but may be felt as an entity capable of dominating what is to happen in a life which may be observed from outside. The horizontal line of psychosomatic medicine is crossed vertically by a line whose origin transcends the rules of time and space in existence.

Any authentic religious experience signals the impact of a transcendental reality on the course of a human life. One may close one's eyes on these things and content oneself with the horizontal; in this perspective, man remains an advanced primate. But raise your eyes to the vertical and you will realize objectively that man has in him, in addition to his somatic and psychic elements, something which surpasses these, which permits him to observe them detachedly and judge freely. This factor, which we call spiritual, makes of the zoological specimen called man a "person."

The unique verticality of the human condition is admirably symbolized by the bronze serpent raised as a standard by Moses (Num. 21:9); in the desert of materialism, the serpents of our animality do indeed threaten to devour us. It is not without interest to note that in Greco-Latin tradition, the upraised serpent of Epidaurus becomes the symbol of Aesculapius which is still the caduceus of the healing profession.

But the stirring end-product of this transcendental mystery is the Man-God, the Healer-Messiah nailed to the cross, from whence he takes on his real dimension, horizontal and vertical at the same time, for the human race. Goethe has said that everything is a symbol, that ultimate realities can only be expressed by images. That is why it is difficult for the human intelligence, essentially causativist, to accept them; that is why they have remained the attributes of prophets, the initiated and the mystics, who have always been treated as outsiders.

But even the strict rationality of an Albert Schweitzer recognizes that all thought that thinks it has reached an end, ends in mysticism, whatever its ultimate expression. Those who have made the "great experiment," as our friend Count Karlfried Dürckheim calls it, no longer doubt that man has a point outside time and space where he may touch in an instant upon all his past experiences, while an animal can only live them as they happen.

The Cartesian axiom "Je pense, donc je suis" (I think, therefore I am) should be turned around to say "Je suis, donc je pense" (I am, therefore I think). From that starting point, one may conceive of thinking techniques elaborated so as to be capable of singularly enlarging the scope of human conscience in the realm of the spirit.

But that is not our purpose, which is to determine the position of the medicine of the whole person in relation to psychosomatic medicine. The latter remains on the horizontal plane and may apply just as well to veterinary medicine. The medicine of the whole person is specifically human but because our mentalities are deformed by Cartesianism and Kantism, it risks being relegated to the altered form of a socio-psychosomatic medicine explained in terms of popular psychology, or of soul-healing by religious inspiration, whether traditional or nontraditional (Jacques Sarano). If the medicine of the whole person is to retain its unique quality and its reason for being, it must not be afraid to make a great leap into the unknown, into a dimension out of time and space. There are more things in heaven and earth than our schoolteachers have been able to teach us. Certain thinkers of our time teach them by extrapolation, departing from actual facts by provisional definitions in the biological sciences.

To conclude, to practice the medicine of the whole person is to recognize in the human being a dimension transcending the naked ape of Desmond Morris, which he is, from a strictly somatic point of view. It is to bypass the usual techniques of organic and psychosomatic medicine, but to recognize that these are nonetheless indispensable to diagnosis. But it must approach man, the unknown, with total respect for his individuality and with a basic attitude of love. Thus it transforms the physician from an observer and indifferent technician, into a brother and friend with whom dialogue can acquire a therapeutic value.

EMMETT P. MONROE, M.D.

General Practitioner
Cuyahoga Falls, Ohio

Opportunities for Medicine of the Whole Person in General Practice

Saturday morning, January 30, 1971: The schedule of patients appears to be a usual variety of medical problems; respiratory infections, obstetrical patients, some minor surgery and fracture care, and a few other miscellaneous complaints among the twenty people to be seen. Many of the patients have uncomplicated problems in which the diagnosis is easily made and the treatment readily prescribed, much as anticipated from the information given when the appointment was made. The person with the sore throat has an easily identified streptococcal infection, and penicillin is prescribed with predictable results. Rheumatic fever may well have been prevented.

Some of the other patients, however, bring some unpredictable surprises. The boy who was scheduled for a physical examination for sports participation at the university is having considerable concern about his ability to let others know his real feelings and is struggling with the problem of developing independence from his parents. The woman who came to get hormones for her menopause symptoms has had severe depressions, with one good and one bad experience with psychiatrists in the past and a disillusioning experience with a minister, and she wishes at this point to stay in touch with her general physician rather than obtain further psychiatric care as she works with her depressive episodes and unmet religious needs. A young man of twenty, back from military service in Vietnam, wishes to be examined because of tiredness. He is apathetic, has no interests, has tried drugs, has no job, doesn't know what he wants. A woman comes in for help with weight reduction and talks about her overbearing husband who constantly degrades her and a fifteen-year-old daughter who is rebelling at every opportunity. She expresses some suicidal feelings, and these feelings must be discussed.

These are examples of the opportunities presented in a day of general practice, United States of America, 1971. Any other day selected could serve equally well as an example with a few changes. How many opportunities are there in a similar day that go by unnoticed or unattended? How many times in a day was I not sensitive enough to the patient's needs? How many times has a patient wished he had been able to talk about more meaningful feelings with me while visiting my office? How often does the pressure of time and the number of patients to be taken care of mean inadequate personal relationships as well as inaccurate physical diagnoses in my practice?

These are some of the things I think about as I consider *médecine de la personne,* myself, my colleagues, and our patients. I am sure that in a medical practice there are far more opportunities for *médecine de la personne* in the day-to-day work than begin to be utilized. Also, I believe that it is I, the physician, who for the most part limit the experience for many reasons such as time and the demands of other patients, my limitations in awareness, interest, and skills, or willingness to adventure into realms where I may not be at ease. Each physician even in general practice limits his realm of practice in some way, whether it be elimination of major surgery, anesthesia, and allergy, as mine is, or some other areas.

Quite often it is the psychological, emotional, or spiritual side that I am most ready and willing to delete, preferring to work with other areas of the patient's needs which often may be more expediently met or may be less demanding of me. It seems from my experience that the patient, when the demands of his need for a more personal relationship become great enough, is often the more willing participant in the person-to-person interchange. He senses this need, consciously or unconsciously, and many times awaits some encouragement or signal that the physician also recognizes this need and considers it important. Many times the most important problem may be mentioned only at the doorway as the patient leaves, realizing his visit is terminated. The patient may feel that to be accepted he needs a "ticket," a physical symptom, for admission to the doctor's office.

Very often I find the most severe disruption in the patient's life may be the most hidden and protected and, until the patient develops enough trust in me, the more obvious symptoms, often physical symptoms, are the ones dealt with first. As an example, with a patient with alcoholism, there may be many visits to the physician for treatment of hemorrhoids or gastritis before getting to liver problems or finally focusing on the most severe problems of the alcoholism. His feelings of guilt, shame and low self-esteem and my feelings of inadequacy and associated guilt may keep us relating only at the level of his more superficial physical symptoms for a long time.

As I consider my understanding of *médecine de la personne* and its application in general practice I think often of the concept of the use of *the person* as the prescription. In a day of general practice I may face a wide variety of problems, and the treatment may call for a variety of different approaches of treatment—drug therapy, surgery, physical therapy, diet, etc., either alone or in combination. Certainly as a part of this list should be use of the person, either combined with other modalities, or as the primary treatment. Very often there is misuse of modalities of treatment, use of an inappropriate treatment due to enthusiasm, bias, or limitations. Unnecessary surgery and overuse of sedatives and tranquilizers undoubtedly head the list of inappropriate treatments, and I suspect that use of the person in most instances is an underused modality. As with any other form of "treatment," it may be successful or it may not be. One may be pleased about the results or may not be, but, as with other "treatments," the success depends considerably upon its appropriateness, proper use, and right dosage.

Only yesterday a simple example occurred. An elderly woman recently treated for metastic cancer was to be discharged to her home after a long hospital stay. Although happy to be going home, and improving satisfactorily, she became very apprehensive the day before discharge from the hospital and called my office at a very busy time asking that I telephone an order for a tranquilizer. After a short talk with her, reviewing our talks over the last few days when we had truthfully gone over her disease

and treatments, she felt things were settled down well enough
that medication wasn't as urgently needed. Indeed, *the person*
was the most appropriate drug.

As I understand *médecine de la personne,* it is necessary for
me to translate it to *medicine of the whole person* as I speak of
it in English. In America we speak often of the *whole* person,
meaning all aspects of his illness, his life, his individuality, his
environment, and his relationships, and there is common understanding of the term. This was evident a year ago at a conference in Majorca when one hundred American general
practitioners and their wives were fascinated by the discussions
by Paul Tournier, Michel and Nicole Galland, and Bernard
Harnik. They were delighted to hear of how physicians in
Europe are discussing ways in which a physician does indeed
become more of a physician and person in some of his relationships with his patients. This particular group, The Ohio Academy
of General Practice, has been interested enough in this goal to
sponsor training programs during the past four years to develop
the physicians' abilities to be sensitive to the needs of their
patients, psychological as well as physical. It was a great satisfaction to me to see dear friends from two groups that have
become significant in my life meeting together to discuss the
medicine of the whole person in general practice.

But what about me, the physician, in the relationship of
medicine of the whole person? The professional relationship is
by nature that in which the welfare of the patient or client is
paramount. Have I received so much that I can continue to give
indefinitely? Do I have the resources and abilities to meet the
variety of demands and to change from one relationship to another in what sometimes seems like an endless procession? Or
will I protect myself by avoiding too much drain? Am I willing
to spend the time? Am I able and do I really want medicine of the
whole person to be a part of my practice? At this point in my life,
my most urgent need, both personal and professional, is for
continued renewal and growth—input of new concepts and
approaches, new experiences, discovering new areas of my own
personality. The usual journals, books, scientific courses, and
seminars have their place in "keeping up with the times," and
many are interesting and exciting, but personal relationships
have the most basic influence. Undoubtedly the medical practice

itself provides some stimulation and satisfaction. Medicine of the whole person is not only for the person, the patient, but also for the person, the doctor. The term *doctor-patient relationship* is often used and little understood as medical affairs are discussed in the United States. Understood in terms of medicine of the whole person it can have a lot of meaning to those who have experienced it as a person-to-person relationship.

From time to time I have felt the renewal and the excitement of participating with a patient in a very personal relationship which seemed to be of real significance to him, and which at times made many of the physical complaints diminish in importance. When this happens it brings renewal and growth to me, the physician, as well as the patient. For me, my wife has had the most profound effect on directions in which I have developed. She has provided an ongoing, loving, stimulating, complementing relationship that has been greatly affirming and powerful in encouraging and bringing out my growth toward a more whole person. The consequent influence has been considerable on my practice, my interest in medicine of the whole person, and indeed responsible for the series of events that led to our becoming part of the medicine of the whole person family. The deep friendships and exchange visits with members of that family have been enriching to us and our own family in many ways.

These experiences and friendships, and just feeling a part of the medicine of the whole person movement, have had a very unusual affirming quality about many things I feel about medical practice. Such feelings seem to be only poorly nurtured in most other medical settings, yet I know they are there with me. And I feel quite sure they are the feelings of many other doctors. The common understanding that breaks through language and cultural barriers, the immediate trust of the people participating in the meetings, the desire to reunite and to introduce these significant friends to other friends from home—all these experiences encourage me to express myself as a person through my medical practice. I feel unusually fortunate to be engaged in a profession that provides such abundant opportunities, and I feel unusually fortunate to be sustained by the rich personal relationships of *médecine de la personne*.

CLAUDE JACOB, M.D.

General Practitioner
Damaris, France

Medicine of the Whole Person and the Working Classes

Who am I to write about the medicine of the whole person and the working classes?

My own class hardly predisposes me to it, for I come from the middle class and am not ashamed of it. I accept my class, to be sure, in a critical and lucid manner, but without pretending to be a "laborite" in an epoch when it is fashionable to come from modest origins. The people are becoming popular!

The child that I was grew up before the war in the very stratified world of a large city in the east of France. I found it quite natural to be one of the privileged, to look forward to long years of schooling, to go every year to the Côte d'Azur or the mountains in a period (I learned much later) when most French people had no vacations.

I was vaguely afraid of men in work clothes, of those communists who wanted a revolution and didn't believe in God. The world of the working man was only something I heard talk about. One day I repeated something I had heard from adults to a man who had been fired: "That'll teach you to drag your feet!" In the presence of the workman, I got a licking that made family history and I learned that here below candor is not always recompensed. Later, walking to school, I looked at the posters of the "man with the knife between his teeth" and feared the street children, ragged and aggressive. . . .

But the war came, I learned history, and many windows

began to open. I discovered and was passionately indignant about the injustices of which the working class was the victim. I still did not know the price of the suffering that had been required to enforce legislation against child labor, to organize unions, to establish paid vacations, health insurance and paid retirement. And it was true that the church had sometimes been the opium of the people, the conservative guarantor of an unjust social order.

Little by little, I began to feel as one with those precursors who had faced excommunication and burning at the stake in the name of science; with those ardent republicans who had attained liberty of the press, the right to assembly, the separation of the church and the state; and also with the small number of Christians who voluntarily suffered abuse and criticism in their struggle to tell the world that the gospel is good news for the poor.

After fourteen years of being an isolated mountain doctor, here I suddenly find myself in my fourth year in the midst of the working classes. I had been used to living alone in my little kingdom, honored and respected, and I found myself brutally thrown face to face with myself in my new environment. I was no longer the only doctor and patients weren't waiting for me. Families tried me one time and then didn't come back. Relationships were awkward and strained, and misunderstandings flourished on both sides. I had to move forward with humility, to observe, to understand, to forget preconceived ideas and yet not prostitute myself. "You can only bring to them what they expect from you"—this from a friendly colleague, who left me to find out for myself what that might be. This purgatory was wholesome, and through my narcissistic wounds I began to have a better understanding of certain realities.

For the laborer, work and salary are the core of life. The work is too often depersonalized and monotonous, hopeless. Basically, the work is disliked; it is considered an inescapable chore and many complain of the lack of communication between people: "We are treated like pawns in a game of chess." The doctor's office is one of the last places where you talk about yourself.

The physician owes it to himself to be informed about labor legislation, the physical and psychological aspects of working conditions, the special nature of female labor. I began to better

understand work stoppage calls, the underlying psychopathology of labor (still little understood), and to make a closer
estimate of the financial and social consequences of my actions.
I was thus led from time to time to transgress the letter of the
law in order to respect its spirit, refusing to be a lukewarm
Pontius Pilate.

And naturally, it is better if the physician's fees are reasonable.
The workers' paychecks don't stretch and we are reminded that,
thanks to our relative ease, we have the privilege of not having
to count pennies. Perhaps I am wrong, but I have never yet
dared to talk with my patients about our relative incomes. This
doesn't mean the worker can't be generous. The humorist was
right who said that the heart that beats under the workman's
cap is at least the equal of the brain that flutters under the
silken shirt of the bourgeois. I admire the smiling strength with
which so many live in a state of complete insecurity, facing each
day with more faith than many Christians who tremble for their
possessions. For a real man, nothing ventured, nothing gained.
But many also—a majority—are engulfed in anguish and depression.

Even when he has reached a certain level of comfort, the
laborer often remains a poor man in our society. He is treated
like an object, moved around, rejected, anonymous, mobile,
pushed into emptiness and isolation. From day to day he suffers
unemployment, displacement, the suffering of his children,
crowded and jammed into mass housing as bad for children as for
adults; I have even seen on the open ground around a large building a sign reading "Children Forbidden to Play." And when they
get to school age, it is hard work to push them until they get
diplomas, the key to social success, while the more affluent, even
if they may be less capable, are sure of comfortable futures,
thanks to their parents' connections.

The worker despises mere words—misty abstractions and
poetry about proletarians. He has learned about life in a setting
where every solution to every problem is fought for every day,
in a society where "everything is regulated absolutely to preserve the reign of iniquity."

What is required of the physician is that he be technically
sound and, after that, be able to understand the problems from.
the inside, without too much talk, to be effectual and to be a

brother. For example, it would hardly be realistic to prescribe psychoanalysis for a worker. That is a game for the rich, who have time to contemplate their navels. For the least favored kinds of workers, the foreigners, the ditch-diggers, all those pillars of the consumers' world who live in shacks, in horrible slums, another step ahead is required: buy a dictionary, alphabetize, give a health card to itinerants, fill out forms, call the boss or the union office, refer to the social worker, work out a viable schedule for visits.

It is true that the idea of class has become less rigid than in the nineteenth century, and an organization stricken by professional defeats and sickness can sometimes be very quickly reduced to nothing. In spite of this evolution, the necessity for class struggle is graven upon the collective consciousness of the working class. This is the result of a long history of betrayal alternating with the use of force. For the militant worker, the strike produces a feeling of rising above his condition, of elementary dignity and a positive affirmation of freedom, of being part of a brotherhood where suffering is shared.

It should, however, be said that the working class has divided into many classes, and, for those who have "succeeded," the temptation is strong to forget the less favored ones. A spiritual, moral, and physical softening is easy to succumb to. As Dr. Armand Vincent said, there is a larger difference between the North African day laborer and the skilled worker who is buying his home on credit than there is between the latter and his neighbor who is the assistant director of the bank. It is this gap which has taken from the labor movement its monolithic quality; it is its great weakness today as seen in the "deproletarianizing" of the upper crust of labor.

As doctors, we are often from among

those who, by birth or training have got the habit of being of the elite, of the ruling classes who are willing to serve sometimes, but as an honor due to their position and not an elementary and simple duty. They think they have no class consciousness because they are socially-minded, fair, perhaps even benevolent in their private dealings, and we certainly will not deny the truth of this; but push them to the limit and they will stop short at the point where the gap is threatened, and the prestige, the uncontrolled freedom which is theirs because of their social position. If one tries to take off the uniform, they think all honor is lost.[1]

I admit having a hard time sometimes making the leap, and I can see the danger in talking about society like a reasonable entomologist. It is the direct opposite of the medicine of the whole person! I am conscious of the fact that the world of the worker has cracked my shell, helped me to become myself, to face my deepest self in a relationship without ambiguity, stripped of institutional pressures. It keeps my face to the wind, keeps me from denying life.

When I find myself at one of our Bossey weeks—so enriching, so necessary and so relaxing—I say to myself that we are, after all, privileged characters and that if our medicine of the whole person is to grow it must dig itself more deeply into social reality, in spite of the inevitable ambiguities.

I still do not understand the working class very well and I know how long a road I have yet to travel, for in humility, I bow to no one. What remains is for me to do my best, to witness to truth, justice, liberty, and love. I know weakness will be forgiven, but not trickery. In climbing back up the path I went down, it will help to be with others who have suffered, workers and others. Christ came to help the oppressed and not "to reassure these who possess and help them to keep quiet those who do not possess." [2]

This book gives me a chance to express to Paul and Nelly Tournier my affectionate gratitude for all they have given me, in helping me to understand others as well as myself. Thanks to them, I can more often see in another the face of Christ.

I think of a thirty-five-year-old man and his wife whom I met during a walk in the forest on a luminous autumn day. We compared our harvest of mushrooms, talked smilingly about one thing and another. And all the time he knew and we knew that tomorrow he would undergo a serious operation which would mutilate him for life. At such moments, one can but be at a loss for words.

Notes

1. E. Mounier.
2. F. Mauriac.

DANIEL PILORGÉ, M.D.

General Practitioner
Mézères-en-Brenne, France

Medicine of the Whole Person in a Rural Setting

Paul Tournier and his school are so important to me on the levels of spirituality, experience, and erudition that I attempt this article with a great deal of humility and respect. I shall try to present, then, a few themes which may serve as background for an essay on the medicine of the whole person in a rural setting.

The first of these is the novelty of this method. I was late in discovering, through my reading, my relationships with others and my experiences, the aggressiveness of my impulses, my thoughts, words, and deeds. I was able thus to realize the therapeutic role of the doctor-patient relationship. "The power of words," says Philippe Kressmann, "is terrible. They can awaken or conjure up anguish. They can plunge one into suffering just as they can bring peace."

Well, all this is not much in evidence. Although, since Hippocrates, the importance of the human factor in medical practice has been emphasized, more and more in modern medicine, purely scientific in its approach, the speed at which we live and the growing number of patients to see condition us to act as technicians only in different kinds of sickness.

Now, sickness is found in the sick and the sick are people. Sickness does not always happen at just any point in the history of the person. It makes a certain kind of sense to him and to his family and friends, a sense that must be searched for if action is going to be taken that will result in a lasting cure. The sick person certainly needs a diagnostician, but he also needs someone to listen to him, talk with him, calm his anguish and help him towards peace and fulfillment.

Paul Tournier, with the medicine of the whole person, helped us to change our lives and those of our patients, far beyond the passing of sometime symptoms. He made us conscious of that solitude which can only be broken when the patient feels he is being considered as a person, a unique creation with his own originality of thought, aspirations, and future according to the divine plan.

The second theme will be the medicine of the whole person as a whole life study. Because he is isolated and has little equipment and few friends in his field, the rural physician, even more than his urban counterpart, must try harder to become a good somatic technician as well as to understand the mystery of man and his spiritual problems. What good would be a practitioner incapable of diagnosing a blocked aorta or a thyroid nodule, even if he knew all about life problems? What good is an internist if he ignores the anguish and disruptive conflicts of his patients? So the rural physician needs study periods in hospital and psychosomatic clinics; good medical reviews, carefully studied and filed away; as well as basic books on the meaning of life; and meetings such as the weeks of study and meditation of the medicine of the whole person.

The third theme deals with some characteristics of the rural setting, the environment and the way of living. The part of France where I have practiced for over thirty years is a region of plains, little villages, woods, and ponds. It is given over to agriculture and the raising of livestock. At night there is a harmony between starry sky and treetops and the whole rustling world of plants and wild animals.

During rather too frequent night visits, the beauty and immensity of creation often invite us to meditate on the fragility of the human condition. "You are nothing, Daniel, and I am everything," says the Eternal, as Jean de Rougemont reminds us. The sense of man's place in God's creation will not be found screened on a background of the factories and skyscrapers of our modern Babylons.

In the daytime, the silence, only slightly disturbed by the

occasional tractor, the peaceful movement of the herds in the meadows, the chirping of birds, the thousand sounds of the ponds, constitute the elements of human balance, a veritable manna of soothing therapy offered by God to whomever has eyes to see, ears to hear, and a soul to meditate. The rural man can easily blossom out in his farm, his house, his village, because there he feels secure. This is indeed that place dreamed of by Paul Tournier, so necessary for a balanced life among his family, friends, and neighbors.

We can bear witness as to how attached our young people are to their country, which they leave with heavy heart, alas, more and more frequently, for economic reasons, headed for the noise and anonymity of the cities. And we frequently see them return to nurse the neurotic depression brought on by homesickness and the alienating influences of the city. Mankind was not made for the prostitution of the factories. A man is a person and rural life helps him to safeguard that person.

Oh, there has been much talk about the hard lives of country people and country doctors, the frequency of home visits, the harassing work, the threat of myocardial infarction and the other difficulties of our professional lives, but if some of this is true, some of it is also false. It is also a problem of organization, methods of work and place of practice. Let us not forget that in the country there is also silence—as Paul Claudel said, "silence which is a therapy, an invitation and a thanksgiving."

Our fourth subject will concern action in depth on the person. The stable rural physician, content, established, an integral part of his community and the countryside, is indeed a man of the earth among men of the earth. He will know profoundly well all those who wish to confide in him, to reveal their problems and their anguish to him. He will often be astounded at his success in working with them and will know how to give thanks.

In order to make this point more clearly, let me tell you a very beautiful story, among others, of depth in action and of slowness in maturation.

I was treating two enemy brothers around sixty years old, one married and the other a bachelor. Victor and Sylvain lived on two farms about a kilometer apart. They had been intensely angry with each other for fifteen years, over a question concerning their inheritance, and they were no longer speaking to each other. This hate between two brothers troubled me, and I resolved one day to reconcile them. Speaking to each one of the fragility of life, I asked them to forgive and forget. "Our days are numbered; the life of a man, you know, rarely exceeds eighty years. How much time do you have left to live? Fifteen or twenty years, if all goes well. What will your parents say when you cross over the threshold of the other world to join them one day? Each one of you will be ashamed of his behavior, of his childishness, of his refusal to forgive. Think about your parents who are watching you."

They were non-practicing Catholics, although they had from their childhood kept a few rudiments of their religion. And they knew, through an entire lifetime of observation, that plant life supposes the existence of a creator, that the seasons and nature suppose a genial organizer, and that the world as it functions could not have been born from nothing. For twenty years, ten to twelve times per year, I had treated one for his chronic bronchitis and the other for his heart condition. Each time, after I had finished my examination and written out the prescription, I said: "Okay, my friend, when are you going to forget your differences and be reconciled with your little brother? The better of you two will make the first move. Your days, like mine, are coming to a close."

And then one day, Sylvain, the bachelor, sent for me on an emergency call. I found him having difficulty breathing, and in a very anxious state; at eighty years old, with his cardiac condition, he had pneumonia. Very worried, I explained to him the necessity for rapid hospitalization, but because of the seriousness of it all, I forgot my usual couplet on "the little brother."

"Dear doctor," he said to me, "all right about the hospital, but that is not what bothers me. I know that I'm going to die. In three days I won't be here. But if you knew, for twenty years, how many times during the night I thought about you and my brother— Go quickly and get him for me so that I can become reconciled with him and his wife and then afterwards I can depart in peace." The moral anxiety could be read on his face. I squeezed his hand affectionately and said to him that God had visited his house.

I went quickly to get his brother and bring him back. When we entered into Sylvain's poor room, the two brothers looked at

each other intently, tears running down their cheeks. Affectionately, they squeezed each other's hands.

"Victor, I am leaving for the hospital, and I am going to die.
Our parents will be happy about our reconciliation. It's still not
too late in spite of so many lost years." Victor embraced his
brother. The faces of each one showed peace. Two old peasants
separated by thirty-five years of hate had pardoned each other
and found the purity of mien of two children. All three of us
intensely felt another presence; the God of Love was in the
midst of us. Three days later Sylvain died in peace and joy, his
brother and his sister-in-law at his side.

The fifth theme will be that of old people in a rural setting
and the surrounding doctors. The rural doctor's clientèle is more
than half composed of aged persons who, born into a stable,
patriarchal society, have now been plunged into a world full of
change with the departure of the children to the cities. The old
person is often isolated in this way. He spends his time waiting
for the visits of his relatives and lives only in this perspective,
often feeling a poverty of affection that he would not know how
to confess. Sometimes it happens that he is frankly rejected,
without love from his own kin. He then willingly confides his
need for affection to his doctor. He is a surprisingly faithful
client. In fact, the rural doctor is often the only person to listen
to him, to counsel him in his interests, and to hear his complaints
about the egoism of his children. One can tell the rural doctor
everything.

By instinct the rural old person knows that parental love is
an absolute and total gift, but that the reverse is far from being
the rule. He thinks that it is thus in the majority of lives, and he
assumes this secret sorrow as a natural state of the human
condition. One must never say to an old peasant woman that her
son is egoistic, for she would not know how to tolerate it; what
hasn't been said does not have a true existence.

To how many children who could keep their parents at home
without too much difficulty have we not repeated the commandment, "Honor thy father and mother." We have seen
orthodox families slip away, while we have admired the filial
devotion of others who call themselves atheists. As Bernanos
put it, it was undoubtedly a question of members of "this holy,
invisible Church which also counts pagans, heretics, schismatics

or unbelievers of whom God alone knows the number."

As to a concrete plan for daily life, medicine of the whole person for aged people, in order to fight against anxiety, isolation, or emotional deficiencies, will necessitate the development of occupational therapists for little jobs, the creation of workshops for puttering around, of clubs, of old people's homes, domestic help for the home. . . .

The rural medicine of the whole person, to be effective, must also keep its feet on the ground.

Our sixth theme will concern the doctor's attitude toward death. The old person, diminished in his physical and sensory capacities, is separated little by little from the world of active work. The idea of death becomes familiar to him. He often accepts it with wisdom, and rarely revolts against it. Certainly, he dreads passing from this world to the other but hopes to find there his own loved ones who have been in the world of God for a long time. We have known old women living in an almost joyful hope in this perspective. "I know," an old octogenarian friend said to me, "that my grandmother and my communion chum, both dead for more than fifty years, will come to find me at the gate of heaven. I am certain of that; both of them loved me so." Absolute love, absolute hope, Wisdom!

One must never lie to someone who is going to die, but, of course, it is not necessary to tell him what he can understand as a person. The prognoses of doctors have only relative value since God alone "knows the day and the hour." Besides, life is not taken away but transformed.

Some weeks before his death from a cerebral metastasis of a neopulmonary, my very dear friend, the rural doctor of the whole person, J. J. Larthomas, wrote me: "You see, friend, one must know how to leave without regret—without too much regret, I mean to say—and above all not to forget to thank the Lord for what beauty, joy, honor this life has brought us. Above all, to live in impatience for the better world which is to come!"

More than all others, the rural person is apt to seize the fact that there is an order of God in this world, a sense of God, a harmony of God in creation. He is thus more easily disposed to the integration of spiritual values which belong to the person.

Dear Paul Tournier, these few reflections have been written at night by a rural doctor after returning from a day of tiring visits taking care of the sick in one of the most beautiful country-sides of France. The author is conscious of the fact that, like his person, this paper consists of little things. "Little things," my fellow countryman Georges Bernanos said, "seem like nothing, but they give peace. It is like flowers in the fields; one believes them to be without perfume, yet all together they are fragrant."

To Paul and to Nelly I offer them with humility, gratitude, and affection.

PIERRE GRANJON, M.D.

Professor of Surgery
Marseille, France

Medicine of the Whole Person in a Hospital Setting

If one considers medicine of the whole person, in essence, to reside in a personal response of the doctor to an appeal from the patient, one would agree that there would be no fundamental difference between medicine of the whole person in hospital practice and in private clientele. Medicine of the whole person is *one*, whatever the circumstances in which it is exercised.

I will limit my subject, however, to a few perspectives of medicine of the whole person in a hospital setting—the patient's appeal and medicine's response—because of the particular conditions in which they take place at the hospital.

1. In a hospital setting, the appeal of the patient is quickly depersonalized. From the bureau of admissions, or from the consultation service, the patient is led toward a service and toward doctors whom he does not know, and whom he has not chosen; there he is subjected to rules and time schedules, to different imperatives which are totally strange to him and for which he can't understand the justification.

He finds himself being examined by different doctors of the service; these in turn seek help from the consultants and specialists; he is transported from the laboratory to the radiology service; his case is discussed in scholarly meetings. But in that universe of chrome and steel technicality, it is the disease with which all are concerned. No one cares about the sick man; no one informs him of anything or asks his advice. Is it possible in this bustle to establish the "singular colloquy" that must be the very basis of all truly personal medicine? An authentic dialogue cannot trouble with evidence, or a schedule. It involves privacy, confidence, trust, sometimes confession. Let's know how, at least for a few instants, to find the time and place to welcome the patient, who needs to open himself up to us.

Undoubtedly, the height of depersonalization is to be found in the hospital rounds, where the chief of staff and his assistants exchange technical considerations which are totally strange to the patient. As they are developed to a level that he cannot reach, the patient realizes that he is the object of medical care, not the subject whose health has been attacked.

He realizes also that he is the object of instruction for the interns. It is about him that the chief of staff is talking—discussing his diagnosis, bringing in hypothetical and sometimes offensive antecedents; envisioning perhaps an alarming or oppressive prognosis. . . . The patient feels disembodied, depersonalized, before this clinical lesson of which he is the object; he would like to understand what was said about him, since he is the subject.

He finally realizes with some apprehension that he could become the object of analytical studies: and, in fact, he is indeed just that from pharmaceutic experimentation to radiological studies, from the operating room where a technique is verified . . . to the autopsy room where this or that error or complication is revealed. And, who could take offense at that?

After all, the hospitalized patient understands poorly what is done to him; he too often is ignorant of his diagnosis; he undergoes his treatment without really knowing either the goals or the restraints. In this environment, this climate of impersonal technicality, this authoritative and incomprehensible world, how could he not abdicate all responsibility and all personality?

He called for help, and he put himself in the hands of the hospital service community, and they took charge of him.

2. Too often, the response to this appeal is equally depersonalized. Too often, the response is purely technical: it satisfies at one and the same time our conscience as technicians and the fundamental expectation of the patient.

But how insufficient this is!

Understood, it is not a question of minimizing the technical role. Medical science remains the primary foundation of the doctor-patient relationship. The patient comes to us for relief, and if possible, the cure for his illness. He is addressing himself to the technician of his illness. Let us remain sufficiently instructed and careful in order to avoid laying ourselves too open to criticism.

But we have to know how to go beyond technique: we must know how to have it accepted by the patient, with its disagreeablenesses, its imperfections and its limits; and its restrictions and after-effects must be accepted also. One has to know how to address himself to the patient as to a reasonable and responsible man, not as to a minor to whom we dictate our decisions arbitrarily and authoritatively.

Our medical technique has to be encompassed with sufficient psychological knowledge for us to understand the patient "in his situation"; to help us interpret psychosomatic interactions; to make the patient participate actively in his cure. Medicine juts out from its traditional frontiers and becomes the "art of loving" which St. Francis of Assisi proposed, in the doctor-patient relationship, on the psychological, social, ethical, and spiritual planes.

There lies the greatness of our task; but there begin the difficulties! On one side, the hospital setting, if it is well adapted to the most secure and efficacious medical conditions, does not favor, as we have seen it, an authentic dialogue between the patient and his doctor. On the other hand, we must honestly recognize all the protective barriers we have established in ourselves, by whatever name we call them, and be particularly vigilant regarding them.

3. Several propositions for a more personal approach with the hospitalized patient are in order here. Each one, according to the place he occupies in the medical team, the experiences that he has lived through, and his own sensitivity and availability, can find the steps he must take in order to bring about a more personal approach to the hospitalized patient. I think that, in a general way, an effort should be attempted (1) by the chief of the service and (2) by the nursing team.

The effort by the chief of service will be greatly facilitated through the full-time exercise of hospital medicine. In order to appreciate the value of the serenity and the efficiency of days in which full-time work goes on, one must have known the regimen of partial time, with its jostlings, the harassment of appointments and telephone calls, the innumerable and irritating losses of time. Full-time work makes possible for the hospital chief a much more personalized exercise of his functions:

—Around the sick. The chief of the service will be able to know them better; to devote to them, each time that it becomes necessary, a personal visit without an associate or a nurse and outside the presence of relatives or visitors, during the evening, relaxed, devoid of any time schedule. In this kind of situation, he could sit on the side of the bed (a sign of availability) and explain where they are in the stages of the diagnosis; or help the patient accept a treatment that may require an undeniable sacrifice of time, courage, or perhaps even an amputation. He will be able, in these privileged moments, to make the patient feel that the ill that is attacking him is his ill, and not a theoretic illness. Thus, in this climate of confidence, the patient will be able to participate personally in the construction of his cure.

—Around relatives of patients. Insofar as possible, and taking into account the imperatives of the well-understood medical secret, it is necessary to let the families be aware of the situation, sparing neither explanations nor provisions, and to view with them the gravity of a diagnosis that may not be disclosed to the patient himself. The family thus instructed can become an invaluable aid to the physician. In this light, I think that the chief of service should not meet the relatives hastily in the hall, in front of the closed door of the room, but rather in his office, calmly and patiently.

—Around students. Students are spontaneously, through their very function as students, turned toward the excessive technical demands of their curricula and the technical knowledge they must demonstrate through examinations. It is advisable to make these students feel that the quality of medicine they will practice and of which they will be capable will depend upon their availability, in all its forms. And in this realm, more than in any other, theoretic discourses are not very convincing: example alone has a true value. It is in this way that one can deposit in the very depths of the student's conscience this germ of a personal medicine, to be developed little by little, unknowingly. Later perhaps it will be revealed in all its force, when, having become a doctor, the student faces his own patients and confronts their problems.

All hospital services should be like a development and propagation cell of medicine of the whole person. Meetings with students desirous of deepening their more or less intuitive knowledge on these problems should be organized and developed in France and abroad. Such meetings have taken place in the past ten years, first at Dieulefit, then at Peyrieu.

—Around nurses. Of all the members of the healing team, it is the nurse who exercises most spontaneously a true medicine of the whole person. Her immediate proximity to the patient and the very sense of her vocation lead her there. Still, she should not feel reduced to a servant's role. Team doctors must explain to her the rationale of the diagnosis, the reasons for the choice of treatment, the difficulties to overcome, the complications to fear. But they must also know how to profit by the observations that she has been able to make in the course of the day concerning the well-being and the different states of mind of the patients she has in charge.

In the foregoing conditions there will be created and welded together a very efficient nursing team. Without defining here the role in the team that each one will have to play, it will suffice to underline the necessity for strong team solidarity. The observations of each should serve all: it is in the course of team meetings that such a joint responsibility will be justified and consolidated. The benefit of a spectacular cure should not be attributed solely to the merits of the chief any more than the responsibility for a failure, indeed for an error, should have to be borne by any one person. The entire team should know, and assume, through the years, its joys and its sorrows.

But, in this solid block, each one must cultivate his own individual availability. When a team member may be more particularly designated, or feel himself particularly called, to take care of a certain patient more personally, because of his particular competence, his affinities, or for another reason, the others should not resent this action or view it either as a promotion or as having been inspired through jealousy.

Finally, the Golden Rule of the team should be founded on respect for the patient: respect for his modesty during examinations, his pain in the course of his treatment, his comfort; respect which must encompass his last instants; respect of course for his political or religious convictions; respect for his preferences, insofar as they are compatible with the cure undertaken (choice of a therapeutic method; choice of a doctor who will be responsible for his care or his operation).

To respect the patient—that is to treat him like a whole person.

Having made these reflections, I have more and more the feeling that, though it is easy to conceive what would be advisable to do to make hospital medicine truly a medicine of the whole person, it is actually very difficult to put into daily practice even the most elementary principles and "recipes."

Medicine of the whole person can easily become at the hospital a superficial "attitude," a sort of medical "paternalism," rather than an élan—a spirit—toward the patient that can bring him an authentic response.

Medicine of the whole person, is, in essence, discreet: it is not seen, it is not demonstrated, it is not spectacular—for the very reason that it can be exercised only in the background, in a climate of confidence, in the growing experience of reciprocal trust.

The hospital is certainly not a privileged place for such research, but it is without doubt the setting in which the patient, depersonalized at every moment and from all sides, has the most need of it.

MICHEL GALLAND, M.D.

General Practitioner
Draguignan, France

Time and Medicine of the Whole Person

The attitude of man towards Time always interprets the meaning that he is seeking to find in destiny, that is to say, the itinerary of his salvation. —Jean LaCroix

To have a concept of Time is to interpret a spiritual anxiety, to pose the problem of the significance of life, and to seek a meaning to the destiny of the person.

The doctor who sees his patients live but curtail the time given to them asks himself about the value of the latter: before and after his terrestrial "transhumance" (or, "migration") man is at the threshold of eternity. Only life has lasted. And unceasingly the mystery of people and their destiny poses itself to the doctor.

One day, inevitably, it becomes evident that personal time is different for the sick person than it is for the doctor. The sick person appears to have time; he has ceased his activity, and he listens to himself, but the doctor does not listen to him enough.

The man in a hurry calculates, reckons, cuts up time: he measures the minutes, the seconds, and even the millionths of a second, and he imagines the infinity of light-years. The child ignores the passage of time: he plays, and, as he does, projects himself into the future which seems so long in coming. He plays because he is impatient to be what he knows he is going to become. "On close examination, life is the conservation of a future," says Paul Valéry. But how slowly one year unrolls when one is seven years old: it is one-seventh of existence, one-seventh of the experience that one acquires through time; and how short is one year seven times seven years later: at forty-nine years of age, it takes only one cycle around a solitary heavenly body to make this man, yet young, a quinquagenarian.

The sick person lives a psychologically different time continuum: he is shut up in his closed universe, separated from and unappreciated by healthy people, little listened to by doctors themselves; he is "in search of lost time," like the great asthmatic, Marcel Proust, who was more sick than a sinner. And it is not certain that "recovered time" may be the cure for him, but rather a different understanding of himself; the perfect "fusion of the ego with which we are born and the ego that we will acquire; perfect fusion which is only effected through beings, places, things—but first, in Time" (Painter). And if a union is not effected between the emotional (affective) and intellectual, there results, according to Eliane Armado Levy Valency, an "interior disorder" which often explains mental illness.

When the doctor consents to listen to his patient, he has to take into account this junction between the two "egos" of the sick person: to do that, he must first of all *be available*. That is to say, he must be ready to vary his personal sense of time and to submit himself to the interior tempo of his interlocutor. There is but one urgent demand, one obligation, one imperative: availability. Medicine of the whole person does not ask for "elapsed time"—time in the sense of duration only—but an intensity of that duration which allows one to enter in sympathy, in similarity of accord, with the quest of the person who, weakened and anxious, no longer knows how to listen to himself; who often deludes and destroys himself.

To oppose prolonged maintenance to brief therapeutic action seems a false problem to me. Both can succeed and help each other.

Paul Tournier's method of "conversation at the fireside" is certainly the most friendly and the most personalized form of the doctor-patient relationship. It demands greater availability, but it also brings a more intense personal element; not only is the time not counted, but the warmth of accord is made tangible in the radiance of the hearth. If this ideal relationship is sometimes possible, it is not the rule.

It is necessary to redefine what one calls the "medical" act. The medical act is a presence, now acted, now lived; sometimes silent and sure like a friendly presence, sometimes audacious and aggressive like surgical intervention. Often too short in the bustle of gray days, it is prolonged by meditation. To be effective, it must be transformed with the understanding of things seen from within (from within the Other), that is to say, from above, through prayer and with the help of grace.

I believe, in effect, that it is a true state of grace which permits us to be receptive; and our transparency brightens the Other. Understanding is not a question of minutes, but of intensity and opportunity. I do not believe that medicine of the whole person must be always made of long and searching interviews; I do not believe that time should be measured, cut up, and paid for, but that time is what is given.

Thus received, will the sick person be, for all that, freed from his anguish? Will he have our serenity to look at his own death, and what there will be after death?

What response then can we bring him? Is there something beyond time? "What relief do you have believing in the Resurrection?" unbelievers ask Christians, and Marc Oraison hopes very much that "transhumance" opens on a different world: a universe whose substance is no longer the same. A world whose creation is finished, where duration no longer interferes to create modification; where life has changed; where the gaze can finally contemplate the infinity of love and the essence of all that we call mysterious and sacred.

The doctor works in time, and time works against him since life always obliterates and destroys itself in being renewed. We call this evolution. The condition of evolution is time. "It is that which avoids that all be given at once," says Bergson.

But our quest is indeed in a hope of another Time, of a world without death, and the contemplation of Love which has conquered time.

BERNARD HARNIK, M.D.

Youth and Marriage Counselor
Zürich, Switzerland

Youth and Marriage Counseling in Light of Medicine of the Whole Person

Whenever one tries to define medical treatment as an art which serves many scholarly disciplines and technical sciences, one faces the difficulty of finding an appropriate name. It is easier to say one is an otorhinolaryngologist than something like a "doctor for the treatment of the patient as a whole man." Even if one uses the concept "integral medicine," it remains to the individual to fill in this notion with his own ideas.

It was therefore a fortunate circumstance that Paul Tournier chose for the title of his first book, *Médecine de la Personne*. This concept, which we want to preserve in his honor, is both more and different than could be expressed by the term integral or psychosomatic medicine. Medicine of the whole person begins with the person of the doctor himself, with his love for patients, his interest and his involvement, with his care and with his intercession. The doctor as a healing factor has been newly rediscovered, but the doctor of the medicine of the whole person does not consider that *a priori*. His method of working will be understood spontaneously, without reflection. This is naturally only one side of his professional effort. The other—one would like to say the objective—side always remains in the foreground, as with every well-trained doctor.

Now the doctor himself is an individual who has a personal history and a relationship to his environment; he is married or single, sick or well—a man like his patient whom he is called to

help. Note this fact: letting the patient feel, observe, and know
him belongs to the work of the doctor of the medicine of the
whole person so that security, self-confirmation, and maturity
will be possible for him.

It is also not unessential how one approaches the patient for a
medicine of the whole person. Of course he must be treated entirely objectively, scientifically, and *lege artis*. Yet, the doctor of
the medicine of the whole person believes that he is responsible
to the patient in other considerations also. He must consider him
as a mystery, as nonanalyzable; and treatable, as a Christian expression, as a child of God. Thus the doctor-patient relationship
can be characterized as an encounter whose expression is dialogue.

In youth and marriage counseling the main concerns are not
primarily medical problems. Certainly there can be something
of a neurotic development, a depression, a schizophrenic reaction,
epilepsy, or some bodily sickness leading to marriage or family
problems, or making it difficult for the youth to find joy in life,
a profession, or friendship and love. In such cases a good medical
treatment accomplishes youth and marriage counseling at the
same time. We see in our practice the reverse effect also: successful marriage counseling can not only favorably influence the
course of obvious psychosomatic illness but also organic sicknesses.

Surely in the case of the application of the principles of integral
medicine, where the patient is seen as a bodily, spiritual, and
intellectual unity with his environment, one will not fail in the
treatment of his patient to come around to the point of asking
about his profession and leisure time, about his spiritual interest
and family relations. If a doctor, because of his specialty, never
has anything to do with the marital or sexual problems of his
patients, then one must justly ask the question whether or not
it would be better for him to be a plant doctor. Now the doctor
of the medicine of the whole person through his preparation for
personal encounter concerns himself with the life problems of
his patient, and he can also help the patients perhaps to understand their meaning.

Many doctors today leave medical school in order to become youth and marriage counselors. Certainly there is a particular profession for that, but one should not entirely leave out a

consideration of the problem of time. While the practicing doctor is often limited in his involvement for reasons of time, the youth and marriage counselor can above all offer time, a scarce commodity today.

For the youth and marriage counselor the idea of the medicine of the whole person is extraordinarily fruitful. The basic problems which emerge in counseling work—anxiety, aggressiveness, loneliness, inferiority complexes, domineering demands, depression, adjustment difficulties, needs of faith, addiction, feelings of guilt, sexual need, and the like—are all just such questions which the doctor of the medicine of the whole person always encounters in the exercise of his medical practice. I would like to show this by a simple example:

As a young doctor I had many occasions to dispense calcium injections. I always concentrated on the careful technique of the injection and on the reaction of the patient. Later when I had come a long way through some personal difficulties, which led to a decision of life on the basis of the Christian faith, I succeeded in reaching a different posture—one which corresponded with what I later found in Tournier as the medicine of the whole person. When I then concentrated on the patient himself, the technique of the injection succeeded routinely—to a certain degree, *en passant.* But the patient's response was changed in such a way that in time he opened himself to me about his life problems.

Now indeed one could practice a purely technical youth counseling. Not long ago a young lady with suicidal tendencies wrote me: "At home the question always arises—are they helping me only for the sake of helping in order to solve a problem, or are they actually helping me for my own sake?" One observes that the person who seeks counsel feels the difference between the objective type of concern by which the patient is an object of helping action and the subjective type which lets the patient know that he is taken as a person into an interpersonal relationship. And, in that God is also in this relationship, the conscience also plays a part for the believing doctor. Yet this is not critical, for it does not come primarily into the doctor-patient encounter. But the knowledge that the doctor is a believer can often loosen the patient's unconscious resistance to the encounter that grows out of the anxiety of being treated as an object of conversion.

I can testify personally that the knowledge of the invisible but present Christ has helped much in the encounter with the counselee.

In marriage counseling an entirely new perspective is revealed if one approaches it from the standpoint of medicine of the whole person. Theodore Bovet speaks of the person of the marriage. He does not only go out to meet the marriage partners in order to understand and to counsel them, but also at the same time the invisible person of the marriage. He conducts a therapy of marriage similar to the medicine of the whole person in medical practice.

I myself compare marriage with a body and can better understand, because of this model, not only the normal development of the marriage (comparable to that of a man in development from childhood to adult) but also the growth crises (comparable to the developmental crises of the individual), and the sicknesses of marriage as well. This manner of concern often succeeds in helping the counselee to find a personal relationship not only to the marriage partner but also to his own marriage. The counselor takes the lead in that he keeps his loving attention focused on the invisible unity of the marriage. His faith in the marriage awakens the faith of the married couple in their marriage. His hope for the restoration of marriage ignites their hope in the restoration of their own marriage.

All that sounds very simple, almost like a sermon. However, in reality it is an event that can be exceedingly dramatic. This drama of marriage restoration mirrors again the drama of the salvation of man. In the interpretation of the medicine of the whole person it belongs with the equipment of the marriage counselor not to withdraw from the great and small dramas. Therefore in the case of tragic results he has fallen no farther into despair than there is again the seed for a new, often invisible hope.

In order not to give the impression that the marriage counselor in the sense of the medicine of the whole person has fallen into some sort of unfruitful mysticism, I remind that he must be technically well equipped through study and experience. In essential detail he will discuss with the marriage partners their problems, helping them to understand themselves and each other better; eventually leading them to an analytical treatment; showing them the possible solutions; standing by them on the thorny way of a hopeless marriage or helping them to make sense out of an unsolvable situation.

If one speaks of "technique of marriage counseling," one must nowadays certainly ask what is meant by that. Under the influence of depth psychology, many marriage counselors have concentrated on the treatment of the partner as the wearer or bearer of marriage, without seeing much more in the marriage than the living room of the marriage couple. Thus it is not so amazing that, with such marriage counseling, marriage difficulties with a neurotic basis are almost the only ones for which treatment is sought.

On the other hand, in Switzerland, especially under the influence of Theodore Bovet, a concept has succeeded where not only the marriage partners as members of marriage, but also the marriage as such, as the body of marriage, should be treated. To give a name to this child: we must call it gamotherapy, and not only therapy of the married couple. Bovet speaks of gamology in order to show that marriage is constituted by more than the marriage couple, even as the body is more than the sum of all its members.

Basically, four rules must be taken into consideration—like the hygienic rules pertaining to the body, and the psychohygienic rules pertaining to the life of the whole man—in order to assure the health of a marriage: (1) the unity of marriage, i.e., the building up of the living partnership, of love, of psychological relationship, of the sex relationship, of parenthood, of the *Weltanschauung* or faith community, and of everyday life (money, profession, free time); (2) the care of the components of marriage: care of the living community, of love, of dialogue, of sexual relationship, of parenthood, of the faith community, and of the everyday life; (3) the maturing of marriage as a whole, which stipulates and presumes at the same time the maturing of the marriage partners; (4) the correct relation of the partners to one another. This provides a classification for the disturbances of the marriage: a marriage becomes sick if it misses one or several sections of the rules of the game or if one or the other of the partners can no longer make up the deficiency.

The most frequent disturbances of marriage are certainly the growth crises of marriage. This does not represent a sickness, even though they can also lead to sicknesses. The first growth crisis comes between the third and seventh marriage year, when many immature factors of partner selection, of love, of sexual relationship, etc., must be removed. After the relatively peaceful middle-age marriage years, a second growth crisis occurs which mostly coincides with the individuation crisis of the individual according to Carl Gustav Jung. But, corresponding to the nature of the marriage as a new entity, it exhibits particular symptoms, of course, which space does not permit me to go into here.[1]

With regard to the behavior of married couples, there will always be disturbances in a marriage where the husband tries to rule the wife, or vice versa; or, where the partners think a self-righteous struggle against each other is proper, or where they avoid the responsibility to adjust. Right conduct comes if the stronger partner submits himself to the possibilities of the weaker, but the question as to who actually is the strongest in the marriage is not so easy to determine. In that the marriage counselor instructs and at the same time treats the individual marriage partner with great sympathy for his behavior, the counselor helps him to turn anew to his marriage partner and in this way to achieve a personal marriage relationship.

Notes

1. See Bernard Harnik, *Risk and Chance in Marriage* (Waco, Texas: Word Books, 1972).

HAZEL B. GODDARD

Psychologist
Wheaton, Illinois

The Meaning of the Person and Paul Tournier

I could neither speak nor understand French. He could understand and speak but a little English so we could not use words to communicate. Yet, we communicated the person in each other and discovered we had a common bond—a unity in the treatment of the person. The translators gave assistance with words, but what we felt reached an area that words could not touch.

Now I must make an effort to communicate the meaning of his person to me and I must use words. It is a difficult task and it is only made possible because we met again a few days ago in Sorrento and the inspiration of his presence is still with me.

I could write this entire paper on what Paul Tournier has meant to me personally since we first met in 1961, but there is no need for that. He knows and I know. As I contemplate and endeavor to isolate the deepest and most important meaning of his life and concepts to me I find it in what he has meant to my patients.

My patients have never had the privilege of meeting him personally but they represent the many thousands of struggling ones who have been strengthened and renewed in spirit through his books.

I am reminded of the lonely ones, desperate in their sense of isolation. He spoke to them with humility and rare sensitivity as he described the loneliness and fear he had observed and felt. Then he gently led them through the pages of *Escape from Loneliness* to the way out: "It is only the spirit of Christ that

can free man from his natural tendencies which separate him
from his fellow-man and enable him to accept and love."

There was the despairing woman who felt she was at the point
of no return in her marriage because she had been convinced of
hopeless incompatibility with her husband. She was given new
hope when she read the lines from *To Understand Each Other*.
"So-called emotional incompatibility is a myth invented by
jurists. It is a common excuse people use to hide their own
failings. I simply do not believe it exists. There are misunderstandings and mistakes which can be corrected where there is a
willingness to do so."

The illustrations could be endless as Paul Tournier offered a
way of freedom from guilt in *Guilt and Grace*, a rhythm of life
in finding a place and leaving it for a new one but, as he depicts
in *A Place for You*, always finding a place. *The Healing of Persons*
opens wide a window on hope, understanding, and infinite compassion.

This is but a sampling of his many books, all of which have
been used with my patients.

For more than a dozen years a group of women have met
weekly, and his books have been the center of our therapy as we
sought "Personality Integration." Often husbands who would not
come for counseling would read chapters that told them *Judgment Is Destructive* or how to *Love with No Conditions* or
revealed to them *My Husband Is a Mysterious Island*.

Many prayers of thanksgiving and petitions for strength and
wisdom have been uttered for Paul Tournier by appreciative
patients.

Paul Tournier is a humble and acutely sensitive man and
would not want undue praise. But I do not feel I am being
unrealistic in the respect and credit I give him, for I have seen
the results of his ministry to the person in the lives of my patients.
I claim only that he has been an instrument for I have felt the
power of Christ behind the man and his concepts. This divine
power is responsible for infusing truth into the person so it
can be assimilated into his life.

Paul Tournier, I leave to others to express the scientific and
philosophical meaning of your life. All I can do is to say what
you have been to me and to my patients—only a few among the
multitudes you have touched in your seventy-five year sojourn.
May God grant you many more!

MAURICETTE REVESZ-LONG

Wife of Tibor Revesz, M.D.
Crest, France

The Wife of the General Practitioner

It is with joy that I participate in the book which will celebrate our shining friend, but the title I have been given for the requested article—"The Wife of the General Practitioner"—leaves me very perplexed. I am sure that if ten women were to respond to this question, there would be ten different responses, depending upon the woman and, above all, the general practitioner. I only believe that all would say that wives of general practitioners must not be (or suffer from being) maniacs, not jealous or desirous of calm and orderly lives.

The wife of a general practitioner must adapt herself very quickly to living in a railway terminal atmosphere, where ringing telephones and doorbells are like the whistling of trains; where there are no fixed hours for meals and where one meets the unexpected at every turn of the corridor—the unexpected from the patient, the unexpected from the doctor. And in the middle of all this confusion she must "forecast" the children's lives. Some wives complain about being left alone to assume the responsibility for this education. Perhaps this is a disadvantage, but many points of friction can be avoided in this way. The general practitioner father, invisible or pressured as he is, most generally commands more respect and esteem than other fathers do. Besides, what freedom of mind, what comfort it is for the wife to have her doctor husband at home for whatever medical decision, serious or slight, that concerns her children.

Availability is a requisite for the general practitioner, in view of the diversity of the patients. Noise and silence must coexist.

It is necessary to have a calm house and a relaxed doctor at the disposition of these anguished, torn-apart, despairing beings, who, however, still place their hopes upon him. And it is incumbent upon the wife to be able to subdue turbulent children or to distract the drunkard who demands a hospitalization document, because anything can always happen.

In the evening, with the children asleep, she must know how to wait patiently for the return of her husband for dinner—late. But this intimate meal has its charm, when it is not interrupted in the middle by an emergency which delays dessert until still later. She must know how to savor the night that ends with a normal awakening, since so often it is interrupted for a faraway errand. And how can she complain anyway of these sudden awakenings since she can go back to sleep while her husband must go out at no matter what time nor for how long? (I know a wife of a general practitioner who said she felt so abandoned after these departures that she always cried . . .)

As for plans, they are always relative to medical activity. How many times have I had to say to the children, "Next Sunday we will do this, but naturally on condition that your father is free"; and at least one time in two, he wasn't. Accustomed to this, the children very philosophically organized something else.

Naturally, the lives of wives of general practitioners differ. My own life in Paris was something else before the war than it is now. No getting up in the night, no deliveries, no office hours or appointments which would demand an impeccable house resembling a secretary's office—of course I was able to be more independent. Since the war, we have been in a very small town where my husband is a country doctor. Here our life is totally different, but we are now a more integrated and complementary couple.

In today's rather breathless pace, how many moments there are "together" when I accompany my husband on his distant calls, the car rolling through the country while we talk in confidence; how many moments of solitude (the doctor being at the patient's) there are when I can meditate or read while I wait for him—a true luxury in our era. I will never forget one night when, having made a flying trip of twenty-five kilometers together into the mountains for a delivery, the baby was late in arriving. The future father provided us with blankets and made a place for us to sleep in a hayloft. We awakened at daybreak and, after the birth of a son had put the whole house into a joyful mood, we had large bowls of café au lait [coffee and milk] in front of a fire. A romantic memory of an unusual occasion—full of warmth, simplicity, and beauty.

The wife of a general practitioner has to be a little bit of everything: the liaison between family, friends, and doctor-husband, who, too absorbed to spread himself here or there, in this other realm of friendship can only harvest what his wife cultivates; the mistress of the house, accepting the dripping or snowy trails which follow the doctor-husband (oblivious to these details because of his long days) onto the polished parquet; the secretary, typing correspondence; the receptionist, understanding and, in addition, sharing many things with the maid, which demands a goodly dose of diplomacy.

From all this there often springs a disagreeable feeling of frustration because this woman is nothing and everything at the same time, always on the fringe of other things and people. By law, she is not considered to have a profession—no family allocation nor personal social security, while the wife of a notary, for example, if she works in the study of her husband, is considered as a wage-earner. People often pity the hard life of a doctor, but never his wife; for her all is natural, including all the extra hours.

I remember one night when my husband was called for an emergency. On his way out, he knocked over an inkwell on the carpet. Already thinking about his patient, he announced it to me with indifference, and then left quickly. I got up from bed, and, crying in frustration and drowsiness, I spent two hours repairing the disaster with two liters of milk.

More profound and painful is another frustration: people believe that a wife shares everything with her husband. But, notice that it is often only very minor things. What is essential to the doctor's life is not sharable with his wife, who runs into a red traffic light burning with his professional secrets. When it is a question of physically sick persons, of course, this is more bearable! Participation consists then in creating the most understanding, refreshing, or compassionate climate possible so that the doctor-husband may be relieved of all worry and give himself completely to his patient.

To have participated at the Congress of the Medicine of the Whole Person where the couple's life experience has so much importance, where the woman at the homefire without diploma or medical culture is received with joy, brings her nearer to the profession of her husband and makes her more attentive to him and to his patients. But, whatever he desires, whatever she hopes for, the barrier is there—impassable between them and her who remains the one delegated to minor things, often vital, but often anonymous. Like Moses, she cannot enter into the promised land of plenary participation. (I know that a friend whom we all know suffers profoundly from it, and I understand her perfectly.)

I would never have chosen to be wife of a general practitioner, and, until the very end, I believe I will have moments of revolt and lack of understanding. Nevertheless, I prefer being a wife of a general practitioner to everything else because it is the profession that I admire the most. For a woman, to admire the life of her husband is always what she consciously or unconsciously is looking for.

This profession, full of fantasy and seriousness, demands of the doctor at one and the same time hours of work to perfect his knowledge and the taking of real risks to his health—nights of slick highways in the mountains, ultraquick meals which can almost be said to have been eaten with a catapult. How can we not recognize the value of this intellectual, sporting, humane and balanced man, never simply "installed," but always ready to treat and encourage those who come to him, staying with them right up to death?

Certainly the profession forms the man. The general practitioner is in permanent contact with the whole man, which can only influence his vision of the world. His existence and, *ipso facto*, that of his wife is more exhausting than that of others, but how much fresher! I admire also a certain unselfishness in this choice. The fact is, and it appears unjust to me, that the specialist in our society is more "honored," in the two senses of that term, than is the general practitioner.

In this rather special life, in this railway terminal of which I spoke at the beginning, where the couple constantly crosses and encounters each other, how many stops are possible between them? They cannot get used to one another since they don't know what will happen in the following minute. But isn't that the condition of love?

To condense this "confession" requested of me into a formula, I will say: The general practitioner is "the adventurer of the modern world" . . . and I love adventure.

ELIZABETH SOSNOWSKI

Wife of J. Richard Sosnowski, M.D.
Charleston, South Carolina

The American Physician's Wife

Today is the nineteenth day of March, exactly nineteen days past the deadline for this paper. As I start over, for about the fifteenth time, I feel a slight twinge of hope. Maybe it will work this time! Though totally dissatisfied with my previous attempts, I was just about to mail "an article" off to Dr. and Mrs. Armand Vincent this morning, simply because I had promised I would "send them something." The postman has just given me a letter from Philippe Kressmann in answer to my letter of apology about the delay of my article. He says, "We discovered that it was a very fruitful strain for any of us to be obliged to put on the paper a little of our experience about *médecine de la personne!*" I had just been rereading Tournier's *The Meaning of Persons* about the person and the personage and discovered that in my previous attempts at this article, I have been talking about me the personage when what I want to talk about is me the person!

First, I have always felt that there is a plan for my life. Most of the time the plan is hidden behind the problems and frustrations and busyness of my day-to-day life. Every now and then the plan emerges long enough to make me know it is there.

Looking back, I can see a thread running through my life having to do with religion and medicine. I remember overhearing as a child a grown-up conversation one summer day. My cousin, an Anglican priest, was telling of a seminar he had been to, in Boston, consisting of clergy and physicians. I remember listening

141

and thinking how interesting it was and that I would like to know more on the subject. Some years later when I was a student nurse doing my psychiatric work at Johns Hopkins Hospital, I was impressed with the fact that every patient with whom I worked had a conflict with religion which contributed to his illness. I could not understand then that the psychiatrists treating these patients seemed to me to be largely agnostics or atheists. I could not understand why the clergy was not represented in the treatment of these patients. I was not especially aware spiritually, myself, but I was aware of some power that was not like anything else, and I was curious. This is not to say the psychiatrists were right or wrong; I am just saying, it made me think.

The thread continued to run in my marriage. My husband is an obstetrician-gynecologist. He is a committed, practicing Christian. He has always shared his work with me and made me feel a part of it. He has asked me for my advice and discussed his problems with me and allowed me to be a sounding board for his ideas. For years he has been practicing *médecine de la personne* without knowing that was what it was. It was apparent that he was helping people in a unique way, and it was meaningful to him as well as to the patients.

Then, we heard of Paul Tournier. During Lent one year, a young priest came to our church to conduct a quiet day. He had been through some difficult years during which he had had a mental breakdown. His face, especially his eyes, showed the strain of those years. His meditations, during the quiet-day service, were particularly meaningful, but most of all, I remember, he spoke from a chair down in the aisle of our somewhat austere church rather than from the high imposing pulpit. He was among us. A few months after this, I learned that this man's wife was a patient of my husband's and that she had a terminal illness. They were a rather young couple with children, and it was a very sad situation, except for the fact that this husband and his wife faced her illness and death magnificently. One day the husband presented my husband with four books by Dr. Paul Tournier, saying they had meant so much to him.

I read all four books one after the other and found them almost familiar. They spoke to Richard as well, and we were both caught up with Dr. Tournier's writing and thinking.

Several years later Richard and I were part of a creative

Paul and Nelly Tournier

Christianity course led by a very gifted enabler, George Kinnemon, who quoted Dr. Tournier frequently. One night he casually asked us how we would like to fly to Majorca to spend a week with Paul Tournier. My husband's reaction overwhelmed me. His practice is extremely demanding, and it is very difficult for him to get away. Also, we are educating our three children, and I was sure we could not afford the trip even if he were able to go. However, it was only a moment before I heard Richard answer George with, "We'll go!" I thought he was teasing, but he was not and we did go. It was a turning point in our lives. After hearing Dr. Tournier tell his story the first evening, we felt the trip had been worthwhile, even if we went home the next day. I was especially pleased that, with my meager understanding of French, I was able to comprehend his address as he spoke and to hear it again as Dr. Harnik lovingly translated. There were two hundred Americans there, and Dr. and Mrs. Tournier were so generous with their time and strength as we aggressive Americans inundated them. The last morning in Majorca, Richard and I were most fortunate to have Dr. and Mrs. Tournier sit at our table for breakfast. I was so stunned I forgot every word of

French I ever knew. However, the Tourniers helped so with their English and Richard with his efforts at a French word here and there that we had a memorable visit. When Dr. Tournier found Richard was a physician he said right away he would send us an invitation to a meeting in Stuttgart the following August entitled *Médecine de la personne*. Soon after our return the invitation arrived and, once again, Richard said, "Of course we'll go, and this time we will take the children." I couldn't believe it. Once again I felt this was "the plan" emerging.

Our week in Stuttgart was the most interesting and happy time ever for us. I was amazed to feel so much a part of the gathering of, for the most part, physicians. At medical meetings in our country, the wives are entertained with fashion shows and coffees but are not encouraged to attend the scientific sessions with their husbands. To be a part of all sessions and even to be placed in a small group and encouraged to participate at Hohenheim was marvelous for me; I loved every minute. My life was greatly enriched by being in the midst of all the loving souls and wise minds here. I came home feeling that even I, a mother and housewife, could participate, to some degree, in the *médecine de la personne*.

Now, I look forward to the next stage in "the plan." Our children will be needing my services less and less, and I will have time for some other use of my talents. I look forward eagerly to the future and more *médecine de la personne*.

SIMONE SCHERDING

Wife of Jean-Pierre Scherding, M.D.
Plateau, d'Assy, France

The Wife
of the Salaried Doctor

For twenty-two years I have been the wife of a private sanatorium doctor who has the status of wage-earner. During this time, I was a practicing nurse for several years, and I could very easily have foreseen remaining there deliberately in order to devote myself totally to the sick.

Hospitalized in a sanatorium because of a long illness, I often saw from my balcony the wife of the chief doctor walking her little dog. She seemed to me to live a lazy life, without interest. I thought to myself, "If I were the wife of a doctor, how marvelous it would be to be able to help my husband around his patients, visiting them and helping them to endure their long months of repose." I did not know that one day I would become the wife of a sanatorium doctor, and, in my turn, I would often take walks with my little dog under the balconies of patients. After my health got better, I became the fiancée of my doctor, who was specializing in the treatment of tuberculosis, after having had the disease himself.

In the course of six months which preceded our marriage, we worked together in a sanatorium, he as a doctor, and I as a nurse. This collaboration was so rich and so fruitful that we envisioned continuing it after our marriage.

Our first year of marriage was not propitious in this intention. We lived in the sanatorium itself, which helped our situation, but I, having become pregnant, had to guard my still delicate health.

After the birth of our first daughter, we settled in Haute-Savoie. The sanatorium to which my husband was assigned was very nice. Soon I could enter into relationships with its patients, going to visit them, taking part in their activities and amusements (little parties, music, etc.). It was a pleasure for me to be in this environment that I had so loved.

However, being rather occupied with my baby and then starting a second pregnancy, it became difficult for me to pursue these activities. At this time, in fact, the contagion of the disease was a real threat, and it was not good for our daughter that I frequent the sanatorial milieu too regularly. Little by little, therefore, I gave up my visits there.

I sometimes told myself that if I had been the wife of a general practitioner it would have been easier to keep in contact with the patients, receiving the clientèle or helping my husband in different tasks. However, up to this day, I have never regretted the orientation that my life has taken, my role as mother of the family having largely compensated for what I had to give up.

My husband has a very regular life, with a rather flexible schedule. He has the privilege of spending a certain amount of free time after lunch, which permits us common and extraprofessional activities. Coming back rather early in the evening, he has always been able to be with our children a lot, following them in their studies and in their amusements. He was also able to introduce them to the joys of nature, to sports, and to all sorts of activities. To this day he remains an excellent companion for them.

For my part, I feel that this collaboration in the education of our children has been extremely precious. We are lucky to be surrounded by excellent friends, all of whom are subjected to the same regimen as we, a situation that assures the possibility of easy and relaxed social relationships. Moreover, both of us having been patients in earlier years, such a relaxed pace has been indispensable to us, while at the same time enabling us to lead a full and rich life. Certainly that is more difficult in the homes where the husband is overburdened with meetings, visits to make, and papers to complete.

We have not known impossible meal schedules, nights unceasingly interrupted by emergencies, annoying departures, compromised familial reunions, the tyranny of the telephone and the obligation of always having to have someone at home to open the door. In comparison, I realize the ease of my life as wife of a wage-earner doctor. I am free from what seems to me an important and exacting part of the task of the private physician's spouse but which would be very hard for me to do: the red tape, the statements of fees, the steps to take to make the patients pay, etc.

Now, after many years of this convenient kind of life, we are faced with many new problems.

Though my husband is not an office worker, he depends for his income on a private group which must maintain a certain level of profit in its enterprise. Now, new methods of fighting tuberculosis are compromising this possibility more and more for the sanatoriums. Thus, our future depends right now on the feasibility of converting the establishment to a medical clinic. That poses great problems on the professional level for my husband. He sees himself obliged to start over again, to acquire new knowledge, to earn new diplomas. He must busy himself with publicity with a view to recruiting new categories of patients; he must visit doctors with whom he must now work; he must attend conventions—all this, of course, while continuing to keep up his daily medical work. Inevitably an enormous increase in work and numerous trips will be imposed upon him.

Even though I can accompany him on some of his trips (a very pleasant prospect, but too onerous to have happen often), I often find myself alone, especially now that our last daughter has left home to pursue university studies. Very available again, I am looking now for a solution which will permit me to be in contact with the sick but leave me time for my husband and my children when they come back home.

In addition to these professional worries, which are primarily my husband's, we live now in great insecurity, uncertain of the future and aware that we may soon be brutally deprived of our situation. In this case, there would be nothing left for us except with regret to leave this beautiful country, these mountains and the chalet where we have known so many happy years, in order to look for a new starting point. In this event my husband would wish to find then an established medical post, which surely shows that he has found in this activity some possibilities for development that he is anxious to renew. And we have confidence in the future, hoping to live this new period of our existence as fully as the twenty-two years which have just elapsed.

JAN VAN DER HOEVEN, M.D.

Pediatrician
Huis ter Heide, Holland

Medicine of the Whole Person and the Child

Children's illnesses are of special significance for the understanding of medicine of the person. Especially with them it astonishes us how difficult it is to formulate exactly the concept of the "person." Tournier warned us with good reason of this pattern. When we become too concerned with theories, the essential element of a matter escapes us. In my opinion we can grasp the idea of medicine of the person only when we realize that "there is no new medicine at all which one could call 'medicine of the person,' but only 'doctors of the person.'" The most significant factor is what Tournier called the inner attitude of the attending physician.

Can anything be asserted on this subject, especially in pediatrics? I am of the opinion that several distinctions on this point must be made, in spite of the critical attitude toward any kind of schematization. The pediatrician deals with three types of young people:

1. Infants and small children.
2. School children.
3. Young people in puberty and in adolescence.

In dealing with the infant, with whom pediatrics begins, can one speak at all of a person?

The young human being is involved in change. He is yet to

become a person. In the first months of life a child comes gradually to a consciousness of his own existence, and then suddenly, only with the first recognition of the face of its mother, something is there, something which forms the kernel of a person. This is something quite different from the recognition of the mother in young animals, and constitutes an essential difference between man and animal. The doctor, to be sure, is the first who comes to an actual confrontation with the human being, no matter how small and helpless he may be. It is here that his calling as doctor of the person begins. He does not only give advice for the nourishment of the newborn, but he also becomes immediately a guide and educator. Naturally the parents are the actual educators of the child, but the doctor supports them in their effort. The famous pediatrician Adalbert Czerny (Berlin) wrote this in 1930 in his book *The Doctor as Educator of the Child*, without knowledge of medicine of the person. He was one of the greatest doctors and a brilliant example of an adherent to the principles of medicine of the person.

All the advice which such a doctor of the person gives for the care and rearing of children naturally goes first of all to the parents. But even here, he speaks as one human being to another, because only when he loves the child as its own parents love it does he find the right tone in speaking with them. That is what matters.

When, as a doctor, he supervises the nourishment of the infant and says to the mother simply, "You have done this entirely wrong," he is still a long way from medicine of the person. Such a statement will shock the poor woman so much that he will have to give her moral support and comfort. He must also muster enough patience to listen to her questions and answer them.

The human being would like to be understood as a person. One must not preach down to him from the high pulpit of the medical profession. Dialogue is essential! Since it must originate about the child as a future person, the doctor should consider the parent as having equal rights with him.

The situation with the school child is quite different. Here one can already begin to build a personal relationship in the sense of medicine of the person.

When a growing child begins to speak, he makes an effort to become a person by coming to terms with the adult world. He is inclined toward perpetual questioning: "Why is the horse brown?" "Why is the lamb white?" "Why can't animals talk?" It is very important for the doctor to know that such questions are completely normal for the corresponding age of the child. The child can conquer his environment only when he questions. The parents, and naturally also the doctor, should therefore answer all such questions in a manner corresponding to the child's age. The doctor should show truly the patience of an angel and not let anything keep him from telling the truth. Only thus can he, in the practice of his professional activity, make the child conscious of his own person, because each child has a presentiment, however vague it may be, of his own person.

The dialogue with the child is a kind of play with question and answer. Though the child is not yet mature enough for many thoughts, it astonishes the careful observer again and again to see how lively his range of ideas is. An example of this:

A mother goes swimming with her six-year-old boy. At the same time another mother comes to the pool with her two children. Little Klaus says to his mother: "Mama, look! The two children are exactly alike! Are they twins?"

They go swimming together. The mother of the "twins" takes out her children, who are now naked. Little Klaus thinks for a moment and then finally says: "Mama, I believe they are not twins after all. They are not exactly alike."

"Yes," says the mother, "that is correct. Perhaps they are twins, but one is a boy and the other is a girl."

Little Klaus is completely satisfied with the answer of his thoughtful mother and plays on contentedly.

One must always respond to a question with an answer suitable to the age of the child. Never say: "You are too small for this, or too young," or, "Don't bother me."

But there are obviously—and one must say unfortunately— unintelligent mothers. To educate them also belongs to the duty of a doctor for the benefit of the child and his growth toward becoming a person.

The third group, those in puberty and adolescence, are met by the doctor of the person in his examination of older school children. When the parents have poorly developed concepts of the child's mind and make mistakes in the rearing of the child, there can be catastrophic results at this age, as everyone knows today. Much depends upon the spiritual attitude of the teachers who instruct the child. Also here one can say again: A teacher should—exactly as a doctor of the person—be a teacher of the person. A human being can come to harm as a person through neglect in all areas where human relationships are important— the worker in relationship to his supervisor, the student with his professor, but especially children in relationship to their parents, particularly in puberty and adolescence.

The doctor of the person should always be available, especially in such moments where the temperament of the young person finds no understanding. In such cases he must be the mediator between the young person and his parents.

A mother judged her fifteen-year-old daughter harshly because she had fallen in love with a young man. The girl stayed out late at night and the frequent arguments with the mother affected her health adversely. Called in as a doctor, I spoke first with the mother and then quite openly with the daughter, during which conversation I treated the girl with the same respect as a person as I did the mother, who was widowed and could not overcome the feeling of loneliness. I was able as a doctor to reconcile the mother and the daughter, and the young people finally became a happy married couple. It is this toward which we strive—"happy children, happy people."

One thing must not be overlooked in the medicine of the person, either with adults or with children: it is significantly easier to carry on a good discussion in the relationship of parents to children when one can appeal to children from the religious standpoint, that is, from the Bible. The Word of God in its wisdom points us directly and completely to the medicine of the person. The relationship of the children to the parents is directly connected to the Ten Commandments and to the desire to follow them. Here lies the emphasis of our time, in which our young people attempt to avoid the commandments in a revolutionary way. What one must therefore make clear to the young people— must attempt to make clear—is this: The commandment to love God and one's neighbor must be viewed as an absolute command. That means: If I really make an effort to speak with a person in the sense of medicine of the person, then I speak to him *sub specie aeternitas*, that is, wherever a genuine dialogue takes place in this way, a third person is always present, the person of God.

PHILIPPE KRESSMAN, M.D.

General Practitioner and Labor Doctor
Bordeaux, France

Medicine of the Whole Person and Labor Medicine

I was still a student when, towards 1943, I encountered the book which was later to become the flag of our group: *Médecine de la personne*.

From the very beginning I had chosen my profession as physician to be the concrete form of my service of Jesus Christ. But I had just run into the positivist, organicist, materialist philosophy which prevailed over our principal universities together with a scorn for personal values, resulting from the parallel rise of nationalism and collectivism. It was therefore with enthusiasm that I discovered in Paul Tournier a doctor who, seriously and without denying Christ, had that knowledge to resolve the opposition between his technique and his faith, between the search for objectivity of the scientific spirit and the deliberate subjectivism of spiritual life.

Was such a harmonious resolution in fact from a Swiss mentality, reserved to the city of Calvin? Was it forbidden in the mother country of Descartes, of Claude Bernard and of Auguste Comte, but also of Calvin himself? I could not believe it.

But how to unite the necessary conditions? Switzerland has always considered herself the bastion of individual liberties. What a distance between the medical liberalism of Geneva, and the social climate of France after the war! Also the fight for a medicine of the whole person seemed to me to have to pass through a savage struggle against all that menaced the "singular colloquy" (G. Duhamel); against all collectivization, against all medical salary-earning and against all subordination of the doctor to whatever employer; against all institution of social security dispossessing its "subjects" of their own responsibility.

Now, in open contradiction to these convictions, from the first months of my professional life, some material observations made of me, one hour per week, a labor doctor! For me that practice then consisted of alternating my services with those of six other doctors who scarcely knew each other, and who never met together. Employees, more or less resigned, marched past us at the rate of sixteen per hour. Wasn't this accelerated succession—which we stereotyped by our own visual acuity and by means of weighing the patients and taking readings of their blood pressure—the exact contrary of medicine of the whole person? To participate in the functioning of this inhuman system filled me with shame and rage; and it did little to console me to know that the miserable salary derived from this parody of medicine left me a little freer from my time with the patients in my consulting room!

But *labor medicine* is another thing than that. And if in beginning I have wished to remember this painful experience, it is in order to be better able to show then what, in twenty-five years, has radically been transformed; and to say why, more convinced than ever as I am of the necessity for medicine of the whole person, I am now happy and proud to be a labor doctor.

To do that, it would be necessary, of course, to be able to trace here the entire history of the intervening changes since 1945 in the regulation of the labor doctor in France. Suffice it to say only that the situation is continually being ameliorated, both in the sense of the independence of the doctor and in the definition of his specific task. His field of action is the study and prevention of conflicts between man and his work—to the exclusion of all therapeutic intervention. (Space does not permit me to show here the negative and positive sides also, of this medical or surgical nonintervention.) Workers are examined at least one time per year, at the rate of four per hour now (count is not kept of complementary examinations or of time used in maintaining records). In addition, the doctor keeps working positions under surveillance, to which activity, according to the law, he owes one-third of his time.

In the exercise of my work, I spend a part of my time with the personnel of a great enterprise of common transportation. For ten years, there have been no more than two doctors for approximately 1,100 employees, as many of whom are conductors as workers or administrators; and I give, personally speaking, 30 to 35 hours per month to our service, assisted by a medical secretary and in conjunction with my co-team-worker doctor.

How different my working conditions are today from those which existed at the beginning. One fact must be clearly underlined: it is in its structures that all work seems to lose its significance. This is why the first objective of the labor doctor must be to conserve or to reestablish, as much in his own activity as in that of the employees of the enterprise, humane dimensions.

Experience proves, however, that, in the perspective of a medicine of the whole person, the evolution of structures counts less than the evolution of beings, than of *our own evolution*. The best work conditions will lead to a promotion of people, to an accomplishment, only in the measure where we ourselves live this personal dimension. And I would like therefore to try to indicate here what such an orientation signifies.

From all evidence, medicine of the whole person is open only to the doctor who recognizes himself *responsible;* only to him who is capable of saying "I", and of engaging himself in his action, with all the risks that carries. It implies, therefore, a struggle against the permanent temptation of the wage-earner always to "cover himself" against the possible errors of his decisions. To exercise medicine of the whole person is, according to the example of the Good Samaritan, to deliberately leave one's mount and one's comfort and security, to go towards those with whom we are entrusted. It is in grappling with their problems to accept, to abandon all prejudice and to show oneself "non-defensive" (Carl Rogers) and vulnerable, in order to better join them in their suffering or in their questioning. It is finally, before all practical problems, to refuse to decide upon appearances or to resort to short-cut and easy solutions, but rather to seek the profound significance of happenings, conflicts, failures.

Such a program strongly risks being pure idealism for the man who approaches it with only his good will. The type of availability, of impartiality, even of self-denial, and the particular discernment that it implies are neither the fruit of technical knowledge nor of simple training. It is rather a question of true spiritual discipline which would be difficult to conceive of without a life of prayer. But it is necessary immediately to add that the richest inner life will never result only in showing us our deficiencies, our laziness of spirit, our blindness in face of true problems, and our radical inaptitude in finding solutions which themselves are productive of new difficulties.

Is it necessary therefore to renounce, to despair? Not at all. For at the same time that we discover our awful inability before the task, we will discover also the incomparable fecundity of teamwork, which alone permits us to exceed our limits. The medicine of the whole person is not an action which would be developed outside of the time and space between pure minds. It is the encounter and the dialogue of incarnate beings, placed in a given background and environment. And our action will not be fruitful unless we are truly beings in dialogue; that is to say, unless we stubbornly cultivate and seek contact and exchanges with all.

Very concretely, before the multiple individual or collective problems, technical or human, which present themselves to him, the labor doctor will remain bogged down in a fastidious and sterile routine if he has not established cooperative relations with Social Security, with the management, with the trained staff and with the personnel—whereas an impartial and attentive listening post for each one creates a new climate everywhere it is established, and sometimes even performs miracles.

To my knowledge, Paul Tournier never practiced labor medicine. But of the preceding description of what a labor doctor should be he has given us the most living example. For since the creation of our disparate group at the Ecumenic Institute of Bossey, he knew how to put us on guard against our simplistic mental reservations, against our prejudices and against our dogmas. He taught us above all to listen to each other, to let us transform each other in friendship, whatever our religious, cultural, or political origins. It is a long apprenticeship that one must without doubt seek during an entire lifetime! If, however, I walk today, slowly, awkwardly, but joyfully, on the path that I have just described, I owe it essentially to the education received from the group of Bossey.

For this is what has opened me up to listen to my nearest collaborators, to whom I had to teach everything. In order that, even in a short quarter of an hour, a diagnostic examination can become the encounter of two men, and so that each one may keep his name, his face, and his life story, the doctor and his secretary must form a true service team in direct liaison with the social assistant who assures contacts with families. This exigence is a possibility.

Yes, the structures of this industrial world crush men, and I have been right in dreading them. But isn't it finally under the irresistible push from the interior change in men, from the biblical "metanoia," that the structures themselves make room for the human element?

GENEVIÈVE JACOB, M.D.

School Doctor
Damparis, France

School Medicine and Medicine of the Whole Person

School doctors from the group of Bossey are afraid of their ability to treat this difficult subject. However, this letter from one of them appeared to give us an exact idea of the way in which, in the perspective of the medicine of the whole person, the school doctor can come to treat the child. This letter also places into evidence the deficiency of school medicine in France, a difficult obstacle for the medicine of the whole person to surmount. It is for these two reasons that we felt we must include it in the homage made here to Paul Tournier.
—Armand Vincent

This is my response to your letter, dear Armand, which has plunged me into perplexity. However for ten days, I have been pondering, as much as I could (Claude doubts it), about school medicine considered from the angle of the medicine of the person.

It is certain that it is good to be inspired by the method of Paul Tournier and of the spirit which reigns in our Bossey, for school medicine as for all forms of medical exercise. I am not a robot; I do not examine machines nor animals. We are very much there—the child and I, and the mother or the father in the case of the younger children—during the few minutes that we arrange for each. Perhaps I should state precisely to you that I have a quarter of an hour for children from five to six years of age—twelve children in approximately three hours. I am informed of the child's tastes, of his reactions at home and at school. Most of the time it is the mother, but sometimes the father if the mother cannot be there, who responds. It is quite helpful to have this idea of the family. And after four years of work, which is not a great deal, I cannot rid myself of the idea that the family is enormously responsible for the psychic development of the child and that equal, democratic instruction for all is a delusion. At six years of age, one already strongly sees the shocking inequality of each one's chances. And what is there to do?

A short conversation with the parents is perhaps a small opening for all of us. The child feels that his parent is looking after him. The parent feels himself to be a good parent; it gives him a certain amount of satisfaction to show himself as such to me. The child speaks to me or draws, generally willingly; he explains his picture to me and often offers it to me as a gift. I show him that I'll keep it for him to see later when he has gotten big.

With older children, nine or ten and on up to sixteen years, the parents are no longer involved in the examinations, and I have six to eight minutes per child. To those who are in prepuberty, I talk a little about their physical make-up, about their muscles, their sports. That is what interests and worries them. They ask me questions of the same kind. I explain their vaccinations to them and urge them to assume responsibility for themselves (their grooming, their annual visit to the dentist, getting their health card at Easter each year and making sure there is no back payment to make, explanations of the vaccination against tuberculosis). At these ages, they are little interested in sickness, but much in their development. Towards the end of their school years, we talk a little bit about jobs, but seven minutes is very short. Luckily, other school personnel can also act in this capacity —an orientation counselor, a social assistant, teachers, and the director of the school. Sometimes the united efforts of all of them in the same cause obtain good results.

But this, dear Armand, is a very small part of school medicine.

The conditions of freedom in which I work permits me the pleasure of conversing with each child. I do this nine hours per week, but I am not fatigued by it. With seven or eight minutes per child, I see twenty-two of them in three hours. That is near enough my maximum that with any more than that I am less alert and aware.

But a school doctor, that is to say, one who works by contract, works morning and evening. Certain people have told me that a few years ago they saw either six or eight thousand children per year. And I see two thousand, perhaps less!

That gave them time to listen to the heart, to check the spine and the skeleton in general, and the teeth, and nothing more. The official journal and Mademoiselle Marie Madeleine Dienesch then having asked them to interest themselves more in psychology, they could see the impossibility of doing everything. Perhaps that is why they went on strike at the end of 1970. The school social assistants have been on strike since January 1971. They say they cannot do all that is asked of them. They give figures. As for me, I am free, but paid very little. If I had to earn a living in this manner, I would surely change tactics; forcibly perhaps? Madie Welsch is in charge. She must see the problem from the departmental level. She has considerable seniority.

In fact, at the meetings of the medicine of the person we speak of so many more interesting subjects but never of school medicine. Perhaps we should have Madie, De Roche, Nicole Galland, and myself get together, and see what will come of that.

But, only to mention—I have only a very limited view—and to send my lucubrations all the way to Texas! It will not be the truth, I fear. Perhaps, dear Armand, you should give up thinking about school medicine in this book. For France, it seems to me that you are happening onto a period of crisis. Tell me what you think after my letter.

I hope you will have a good rest at Céreste, and that both of you can really relax.

Geneviève.

LOUIS BERGOUIGNAN, M.D.

Surgeon
Evreux, France

Surgeons and Medicine of the Whole Person

A boat, somewhere on Lake Lucerne . . . On this boat, "the guiding team" of Bossey's group, united around Paul Tournier to prepare the session of the following year. One of us proposes a subject which will only allow philosophical, psychological, and psychoanalytic conferences. . . .

Then, Paul hits his fist on the table, and says: "Not too much philosophy—without that my surgeons are going to break up the group—"

Excuse me, Paul, if I concern you so directly, but I, as a surgeon, have been so struck by your friendliness and interest that I could not help recounting this anecdote that I remember from the chapter entitled "Surgeons and Medicine of the Whole Person."

Yes, why do so many surgeons, and not the minor ones, regularly and faithfully go to Bossey's meetings? What do they have to learn there, for themselves, for their patients? What do they have to bring to their colleagues of other disciplines? That is what I would like, in a few pages, to try to analyze.

Surgery and the psychosomatic have already been spoken of for many years. My friend Jean Gosset was one of the first, if not the first, to enlist the services of a psychiatrist for his patients. Coldefy, a surgeon from St. Anne, wrote a book entitled *The Psychosomatic and Surgery*. At the Surgical Congress in September 1970, a colloquy, resumed a few weeks later by French television, united surgeons and psychiatrists.

160

I really believe that a surgeon, as able and conscientious as he may be, cannot be entirely satisfied with his surgical act alone. How does one explain certain bad results that come to light after the best of interventions; in particular, in digestive, gynecological, and orthopedic surgery? My operative indication was clear; there was an evident anatomical injury; technically, I gave the best of myself; the immediate operative consequences were exemplary. But several months later, this same patient comes to my office to tell me of his dissatisfaction, and to ask me again for treatment.

It is, I believe, only at the end of a career, when one has really wanted to examine his failures and try to determine the cause of them, that one can begin to see clearly. And, there is no doubt that, for me, as for many others, the light began to shine after I met Paul Tournier, read his books, went to Bossey's meetings. It was then, with the help of other surgeons and doctors, that I was able to realize that the surgical act alone was but one part of the healing. But above all, I came to realize that I should not limit myself to be only the head which directs and the hands which operate, and leave the rest to my colleagues, anesthetists, nurses, the doctor on call, or even a psychiatrist. I should learn to become, myself, a healing instrument, bringing to my patient my whole being, not just my hands and my brain. It was then that an entirely new surgical perspective was opened up to me. Now I attribute much more importance to the preoperative consultation, even if the patient arrives with a letter from his own doctor and a predetermined diagnosis.

Here is a woman around thirty years old who was sent to me for a hysteropexy. She has been suffering for years, not only during her menstrual periods, but also when she works standing up. She doesn't tolerate sexual relations with her husband easily, her character is turning sour, and her marriage is in danger. Of course, a good hysteropexy will take care of all that; once the uterus is put back in place, her periods will become normal, her pelvic area will no longer be painful.

I operate—the uterus was greatly tipped, the adjoining parts healthy—an easy hysteropexy, completed with an appendectomy. Ten days later the patient goes back home, confident and reassured.

Three months later, I find her in my office, desperate. "It's just like before—I'm sorry I was operated on." Then later, in the course of one of many conversations which should not be an interrogation, I learn that before the marriage there were some genital and moral traumas which had profoundly marked the patient. I learn that her husband, who does not want to get old, and who does not know how to "change his speed," has faced her with daily demands that she no longer can accept and which, little by little, make her regard the sexual act in horror. And my hysteropexy didn't change anything at all.

It is then that, knowing what I know, I can be able, perhaps, to arrange things, by having a long and precise conversation in private about it with the husband and putting it "on the line," with the authorization of the couple, the assisting doctor, and, eventually, a psychiatrist. But shouldn't I have had to do all of that before operating?

Here is another patient who arrives with a letter from his doctor and an enormous package of x-rays. He has had a duodenal ulcer for years. He has followed, seriously, diets and medicine, and, of course, between each attack he had been better. But the attacks came closer and closer together, his general state of health is impaired, work becomes painful, and frequent days off put his material situation in danger.

I'm asked to operate, and I accept. I will choose, of course, according to the case, the position of the ulcer, my experience and my habits, the best technique; it doesn't matter much, I believe, since all techniques, even the best performed, can be followed by failures.

And it's the same scenario as before! Easy operation, departure from the clinic with many thanks—and the return to the office a few months later, with demeanor sad and glum . . . "I'm still suffering!"

And there also, I learn that the patient has been worrying for a long time about his employer, his colleagues, his wife, his children. He smokes too much, and drinks occasionally. Once I operated on a night watchman who, when he returned in the mornings to his two-room apartment, found his wife and his three children awake. How could he relax—the bad operative consequences were transformed from the day when I could obtain for him a larger lodging with an isolated room for him.

Here are many other patients—I think about those injured in

traffic accidents, or at work, that I see as an expert. For a nearly identical injury, correctly treated, osteosynthesized, the relapses are absolutely different from one patient to another. I'm not talking, of course, about those who willingly overrate their relapses in order to obtain a stronger indemnity; an expert who knows his profession will soon have those tracked down.

Rather, I think about the injured or about the orthopedic patients who don't have any pension to look forward to. Certain patients, even the young, shut themselves up in their sickness and will not make even the slightest effort to recuperate. Others, on the other hand, full of activity, of energy, of strong will, confident in the future, in their star, become so much better that, in spite of their evident infirmity, one would have to be tempted to speak of their healing. Suzanne Fouché, who has a lot of experience about these questions, will surely not contradict me.

But, there still, does not the surgeon have for his mission not only to try to reestablish to the best of his ability the anatomy and bodily function, but also to penetrate more intimately into the life of his disabled patient—to know what he will find at his home after leaving the hospital, what moral help his family or friends will bring him? Will he remain alone to think over his troubles while standing out in the sun on his doorstep, making only a few prudent steps with his two crutches, and that over a period of months? Or rather, to the contrary, will he try from hour to hour, from day to day, to work—to regain a new degree of flexion and extension, even at the price of pain—in short, to win a victory over himself and his infirmity?

I was mutilated in the war in 1944, when a bomb explosion modified my anatomy a little, and, in particular, carried off my left eye. For a surgeon, that is fairly disagreeable. But I will always remember when, coming back to the Academy of Surgery for the first time, I met there Louis Bazy, who had also lost an eye, but nevertheless magnificently continued his profession. That day, he had been for me, without knowing it, a true doctor of the whole person; he told me his story, explaining how he had been reeducated and had resumed his profession.

That very evening, all fired up, I went home and began my own reeducation—it's been twenty-six years of just that—and I can say that I consider myself to be *healed* as long as, of course, my remaining eye continues to function well. In fact, I am often sent despairing one-eyed people so that I can encourage them and help them profit by my experience.

Surgeon of the whole person? These are big words, indeed; it's not necessary to exaggerate. One should not, above all, without being prepared, be pretentious enough to play the role of psychiatrist. We would then risk being a sorcerer's apprentice who could perhaps launch a serious crisis.

But, through our personal experience, our attitude, the love for our patients, and through our research of all that concerns them— not only anatomical injury but also personal problems—we can surely give to those who confide in us much more than they normally expect from our scientific and manual abilities.

This is, I believe, a work for all time. It begins with the preoperative consultation and continues through the reception at the clinic, during the course of the treatment itself and also every day that follows, when the visit and the countervisit should not be limited to technical acts and terminology alone. The patient should have the impression that he is our only patient, and that we will bring to him through thought and deed, the best of ourselves.

One of us wrote: "The medicine of the whole person begins through the person of the doctor." Thus, we risk the words: surgeon of the whole person, why not!

KURD VOGELSANG, M.D.

Professor, Ophthalmologist
West Berlin, Germany

Medicine of the Whole Person and Ophthalmology

To take sick people into consideration on their physical, psychic, and spiritual levels—this is medicine of the whole person. —H. Mentha (1947)

The situation of medicine in the last third of the twentieth century can be compared to six flowing rivers which meet together in a delta. These are: physiology, pathology, biochemistry, genetics, surgery, and therapy. During his time of education the beginning doctor will be theoretically and practically instructed in these six disciplines, so that he can later practice the profession of doctor.

Is everything included here which the doctor will need for his contact with the patient?

One must grant that the progress of medicine has doubled life expectancy in the last hundred years; that modern surgery has developed in a way which no one could have foreseen; that psychology accomplishes what comes to the mind!

And yet there remains a remnant of dissatisfaction of being, for both doctors and patients.

It is always well worth noting that the personality of the doctor plays a great role. On the one hand it can produce a particularly specialized and technical knowledge without a *Weltanschauung* or religious connection. On the other hand it can be joined with the gift of feeling and human leading. Here the role of the present-day family doctor must be mentioned.

As a representative of ophthalmology, I would like to focus

attention on this discipline. This oldest specialty of medicine has in the previous one hundred years conformed to all stages of development of scientific medicine. The operative procedures for glaucoma have been improved, so that the risk has been diminished. The cornea transplant with the difficult replacement of the frontal pieces of the eye can give possibility of vision again. We should especially mention the possibilities of the retina's taking root by operative procedures (success quota over 50 percent). The severity of infectious eye diseases has been strongly reduced; treatment of squinting has reached a new stage through treatment of the amblyopic eye. The optical industry manufactures visual aids of the widest variety. Who would not rejoice over the progress and success in the interests of eye patients?

As a second step, one can mention psychological medicine. Medical science has produced a significant development here also.

The student has already been introduced to new formulations for school medicine. Thus writes the Basel professor F. Rintelen in 1969 in his textbook of optical medical science: "When the symptom is correctly identified, so-called simple conjunctivitis is frequently the first impetus to a necessary psychological treatment. The neurotic overvaluation of absolutely harmless bodily changes in the eye, which stands so near to our 'ego-feeling,' to our egocentric localization, is often the result and expression of a psychological need. More often one can speak in individual distinctive cases of an organ neurosis, or even of a psychosomatic disturbance. The establishment of human contact, the intelligent discussion of the life situation not only can improve the bad feeling in the area of conjunctivitis but also contribute to the reduction of neurosis."

More attention is currently being given to psychohygienics of the eye, and not only in the case of glaucoma. Fatigue associated with work or with watching television plays a decisive role, as do aspects of occupational medicine (blinding, special lighting, etc.).

The central tasks of psychological medicine in optical medical science lie in the care and control of the cross-eyed (orthoptic treatment in vision schools), of those to be operated on, the one-eyed, those deformed in the face, the amblyopic, and the blind.

In the education of an eye doctor, value must be placed on psychological schooling; he must know what is understood with a little psychotherapy and have the knowledge to handle it. Leading a conversation demands schooling; the sensible eye patient is entitled to help. Injuries (for example, through diagnosis by liquidation or listening to dictations of findings) are to be avoided; psychological help through encouragement is an interhuman command.

Every calm conversation brings to light new and important perspectives of the patient's prehistory or of therapy (for example, allergy) and unites the doctor more closely with the patient, his family and his fate. The doctor must always make it clear that the removal of a foreign body from the eye or the diagnosis of the first glasses for the patient can be a psychological burden, factors which to a great extent no longer come into the doctor's awareness.

We have known all this for generations, of course, but even with the best of intentions we do not have the time to busy ourselves with patients as we should. But there are often little things we can do: for example, by sitting down next to the patient for only a minute one can turn to him more than in standing; or one can note himself the times for important consultations (such as determination of the viewing field or measurement of pressure on the eyes).

Much can be taken up by the co-workers—a secretary who knows how to ask questions sympathetically, and the nurse who spends much more time with the patient than does the doctor. With the building up of a practice, the doctor will, where possible, train his co-workers quite consciously in the mentality which he represents.

Remember the words of the Swiss eye doctor Marc Amsler (1949): the body-soul problem concerns the eye doctor also.

Still we must go a step higher. Can the medical-school doctor or the psychological doctor dispute that there is still much between heaven and earth which he does not know? Can also the disciple of Rudolf Virchow or the student of the great Swiss physiologist W. R. Hess deny that we still know little about many essential questions? Certainly each of them will go the way taught him by his teacher—the former, the pathological; or in the second case, exact neurophysiological research. It is equally important that present-day young researchers should go to work with the same diligence and wealth of ideas.

There still remains something which we can for the time being neither research nor know, but whose existence is experienced. Everyone must also enter into a discussion with death. If we have reached the threshold of faith, should we not step over it gladly, conceding and affirming thereby the experience of transcendence?

In some sicknesses there is a course of healing which we cannot grasp. There are effects of man to man with which we can measure no physical waves. There is the experienced effect of prayer. There is the gift of religious influence. Does not all this belong in medical science?

Thus we have reached the last level of the steps and are in the working territory of the medicine of the whole person. It is true grace which has brought Paul Tournier to his conception and his diligence to give it further to others.

If the doctor-patient relationship is lifted to the high plane of faith and transcendence, a durable basis is created which can bear heavy burdens. Every doctor needs for his bad results a gracious God, and what a great experience it is if he experiences the patient as brother. There arise then new possibilities of common consultation over the successful measures of healing and the help of a prayer community.

Certainly we must again reckon with objections: "We want no criticism, no pessimism; we wish pure separation of medicine and religion." "We have a model social state; we have always had doctors as you have described them."

Paul Tournier has established the medicine of the whole person on the basis of school medicine, modern psychological medicine, and biblical doctrine. His lectures, his books and his Bossey group exercise a great influence.

The medicine of the whole person is the seventh stream which flows together into the above-mentioned six tributaries. Universal medicine now contains its entire fullness and power.

Immense work must be performed for the future so that as many doctors as possible can be filled by this totality and use it. In study time and further education they must add the knowledge currently belonging to it to what they already possess.

Through more work and joyous attention we can thank Paul Tournier for his life work and be faithful to him.

WILLIAM W. McLENDON, M.D.

Pathologist
The Moses H. Cone Memorial Hospital
Greensboro, North Carolina

Medicine of the Whole Person and the Laboratory Physician

Keith Miller has said that when he first met Paul Tournier he felt that he had had an encounter with "walking love." No better description could be given to Paul Tournier and the influence he has had in my life. My contacts with Paul and Nelly Tournier have been limited by space and time to only four memorable occasions—in 1961 and 1965 when they toured the United States, in 1962 when I attended the Bossey Group meeting at Bad Boll, and in 1970 when my wife and I attended the Word Tour "Adventure of Living" seminar in Majorca. The opportunity to be with the Tourniers at Bad Boll and again at Majorca came at times in my personal and professional life when I was in a state of despair and indecision about the future. My attendance at these two meetings came after a series of coincidences which I now sincerely believe were the hand of God leading one of his reluctant servants. For after these two encounters with Paul and Nelly Tournier and their associates, I was propelled from a state of depression to a new level of enthusiasm for the adventure which was possible for me in both my personal and professional life if I would but let God be my guide.

In the ten years since I completed my professional training in the specialty of clinical and anatomic pathology in 1961, I have had the exciting and challenging opportunity to practice laboratory medicine in two active modern hospitals—first in a U. S. Army Hospital in Germany, and since 1963 in the Moses H. Cone

Memorial Hospital in Greensboro, North Carolina. My real introduction to the medicine of the whole person came at Bad Boll in 1962, but for some time it seemed to me to have application only in the traditional setting of the physician and his patient in the home, doctor's office, or hospital room. Yet as I experienced on a day-to-day basis the needs and challenges of the practice of medicine in a large and increasingly complex hospital, I realized more and more the need for a broadening of the concept of medicine of the whole person to include the newer approaches to medical care. In my reading and meditation, I realized that this was not foreign to Paul Tournier's concept, for he has said that *médecine de la personne* is not some new specialty but rather is the "commitment of the person of the doctor himself" to his patient and his practice. Such a commitment of the person of the doctor can occur not only in medicine and surgery but in any setting where the physician is willing to commit both his scientific knowledge *and* his own person to benefit the patients he serves.

The discussion which follows represents my concept of the role of the laboratory physician in the practice of medicine of the whole person in the modern hospital based on my experiences in such a setting during the past decade. It is dedicated with sincerest appreciation to Paul Tournier on his seventy-fifth birthday.

At the turn of the century the hospital was a simple organization with personal interactions essentially limited to the patient, the nurse, and the physician. The hospital was usually in a small building (frequently a converted house) with a small staff and provided only a small part of the total medical care for a community. Today the modern hospital and the related health care facilities represent a large investment of public and private funds in buildings and equipment and employ numerous people in an ever-increasing number of specialized health-care occupations. The mission of the hospital is no longer just to give custodial care to those with terminal illness but to provide active treatment for all types of illnesses, both physical and mental. Today the hospital and medical community generally is being challenged to be concerned not only with the severely ill "horizontal" patient, but to be concerned with prevention of illness and with the detection and treatment of early disease in the "vertical" patient.

As a result of these many changes during this century, the hospital has become a focus of community interest and concern because of its manifold influences in the lives of so many persons. Anne R. Somers has very clearly stated the far-reaching implications of these changes when she said in the Seventh Annual Herman Cone Lecture: "The hospital is to modern America what the cathedral was to Europe in the Middle Ages."

In spite of the many advances in science, technology, and management which have been applied to provide modern medical care facilities, many a patient must feel as if these facilities were some impersonal giant designed to frustrate and impede his progress toward the cure of his illness and his return to productive life. The person who is depressed and bewildered by his illness may well come away from our hospitals with a sense of loneliness and anger because he was not respected as a person, even though he received the very best scientific medical treatment.

Paralleling the development of scientific medicine and the evolution of the modern hospital has been the development of many specialties in medicine. In addition to the various subspecialties which have evolved from medicine, surgery, and pediatrics, a number of specialties have evolved because of the needs of the modern medical center: laboratory medicine, radiology, nuclear medicine, emergency medicine, biomedical engineering.

The role of the pathologist or the laboratory physician in its modern sense is a relatively new one when viewed in the light of the centuries of medical history. However, when pathology is defined in its broadest sense as the "study of disease" then all physicians worthy of the name are "pathologists" in the tradition of Sir William Osler, who used the laboratory and post-mortem study of disease as a means of improving his ability to help the sick person before him. The specialty of pathology evolved from the work of Morgagni, Virchow, Rokitansky, Welch, and many others who used the study of post-mortem changes to understand the mechanism of disease. Since the hospital in the nineteenth and early twentieth century was frequently a place one went to die, the pathologist became the curator of the "death house," and his major concern was with the post-mortem changes of disease. His motivation was excellent as was shown by the following motto which was frequently displayed in the autopsy room: "Hic est locus ubi mors gaudet succurrere vitae" (This is the place where death rejoices to come to the aid of life). Nonetheless, one wonders if the study of post-mortem findings did not become for many pathologists an end in itself and an escape from the responsibility of dealing with the real problems of the live and suffering patient. Because of this long separation of the practice of pathology from the mainstream of medical practice, many older physicians even today express surprise when they discover that the laboratory physician is genuinely concerned about a clinical problem.

The evolution of modern scientific medicine has given the pathologist the opportunity to study the early changes of disease chemically and morphologically by histochemistry and by light and electron microscopy in biopsies and cytological preparations. He now has the opportunity to correlate clinical, biochemical, and morphological changes of disease in the living patient. He has been challenged to put to use the knowledge and techniques of nuclear physics, automation, and computer technology in his clinical laboratory.

The role of the laboratory physician has changed radically in the last several decades because of the changes in the nature of medical care and the changing role of the hospital. He has been challenged to step out of the death house and into the clinical arena where he is increasingly becoming a partner with the clinician in the prevention, detection, and treatment of disease. His laboratory is becoming a means by which disease is detected in an earlier and earlier stage and where the progress of treatment with the newer and more powerful agents and techniques is monitored. The autopsy remains an important educational activity for the entire medical community, but, for the pathologist, it has now become only one of very many methods by which he contributes to better medical care for the community of patients he serves.

The function of the laboratory physician in his new role spans both the academic and scientific community and the clinical community of the applied medical sciences. In the former he is striving to achieve the goals of the academician and scientist with their concern for the discovery of new knowledge and the education of students who are to furnish the manpower for the medical care of the future. In the latter role he is concerned with all that influences the course of those patients to whose care he contributes. His unique mission is to take the advanced knowledge and techniques from the basic and applied sciences such as chemistry, physics, biology, and electronics and apply them to aid his fellow physicians in their efforts to preserve the health of their patients.

As a scientist, the laboratory physician is not turning against God but is an adventurer with God, as Paul Tournier has so eloquently stated in *The Adventure of Living*:

> Every new discovery of science brings to light an original invention by God, an ingenious solution found by him to each of the technical problems raised by the functioning of the world and of all its component parts, of all the heavenly bodies, of all the physical and chemical reactions of matter, and of every living organism.

As a physician concerned with the healing arts, the laboratory physician joins his colleagues as a co-worker with God. Again, to quote Paul Tournier:

> It has been said of medicine that its duty is sometimes to heal, often to afford relief, and always to bring consolation. This is exactly what the Bible tells us that God does for suffering humanity. Sometimes God heals, but not always. But he gives relief, He protects and sustains us in times of affliction; and His consolation is unending. Here too we may say that the doctor in his vocation works hand in hand with God.

As a bridge between the scientific community and the healing community, the laboratory physician by his life and work has a unique role to play in the modern medical community. He is in the position to insist on the finest scientific medical care for those he serves while at the same time insisting that this care be delivered in an atmosphere of personal concern for each patient served *and* of mutual respect for each of his co-workers in the health field. Because he is usually based in the hospital (and along with the radiologist may be the only physician so situated in smaller hospitals in America) he has the opportunity to influence the attitudes which prevail in the entire hospital. His role can be especially vital in influencing the attitude of other physicians and of those in administrative positions toward the hospital staff. In the machine shop the worker who is mad at his boss can express his hostility by hammering harder on his work. The hospital worker who is not treated with respect and concern, however, expresses his anger and frustration in his contacts with the defenseless patient whom he is supposed to be serving. Although the physician and nurse still have the primary influence on the patient's course, I do not believe one can overestimate the positive healing influence of the cheerful and concerned janitor, aide or orderly, laboratory technologist, or physical therapist. This attitude of respect for the person of the patient comes to the students and hospital staff through the example of the physicians and supervisors with whom they have contact. Because of his daily presence in the hospital and his concern with both the science and the art of medicine, the laboratory physician has a unique opportunity to influence positively the attitude of those groups.

In this age of increasing instrumentation, automation, and computerization of medical care the laboratory physician also has another opportunity to be of service. Through his knowledge of science and technology and his contacts with persons in these areas he can be of assistance in the wise use of these powerful tools so that they benefit patient care. Just as importantly, he is in the position to ease the transition from the old to the new for those on the medical and hospital staff who are threatened by these new approaches. He is faced with the challenge to see that these new techniques are designed and used to do those things that the machine can do best while freeing the physicians and hospital staff for those intellectual and personal tasks which no machine can do.

If medicine is to succeed in meeting its challenges, modern hospitals and medical centers must become places where persons are healed rather than places where diseases are treated. The laboratory physician who is willing to commit his knowledge and skills as well as his own person to the practice of medicine of the whole person can play a major role in this process.

ISOLDE EMICH, PH.D.

Psychologist and Specialist in Readaptation
of Retarded and Inhibited Children
Vienna, Austria

Rehabilitation and Medicine of the Whole Person

By his commitment man manifests his humanity.
                                        —Paul Tournier.[1]

In the life and work of Paul Tournier road signs shine everywhere which lead directly into rehabilitation of the most severely injured. Commitment, accomplishment as an endowment of humanity—the choice of this leitmotif was difficult. For in all the writings of Paul Tournier the important thing is readiness, surrender, commitment of the entire man—commitment in relation to others, to God, to oneself—both in a broader and in a narrower sense. The person undergoing rehabilitation experiences it more strongly than the invalid; for him everything essential is, as it were, emphasized. Commitment is a password for the daily, nightly, hourly new dangers, difficulties, pains, humiliations, for the new beginnings. The severely injured person also knows passionate search for God better than the invalid knows it; the latter can recover, but the rehabilitated handicapped person remains at best a no longer handicapped blind person, one without hands perhaps, or paralyzed. "To live is to choose."[2] Life is self-decision. The trauma of the injury or sickness cannot simply be obliterated. Often, after decades, we scarcely look back upon illnesses we have gotten over. But the psychosomatic disability of the badly injured person remains present. Brought freshly to recollection in the morning with each awakening, it is ex-

175

perienced, lived through, overcome, ignored countless times during the day. The minus must become a plus. That happens in a total rehabilitation, in which "total" is to be related not to that which is physical but to that which is spiritual.

We all have "necessary times of maturing."[3] A need is to be fulfilled, a healing is to be attained. Maturing means becoming different, enduring. The severely disabled person has his additional times of maturing. Maturing means always "to look forward and not back." [4] Paul Tournier says this in relation to the seasons of our life. The handicapped person, one can probably add, has his additional seasons, analogous to his additional times of maturing. At times it takes years or decades, at other times it comes like a revelation, a sudden phenomenon. It is a matter of rebirth, of becoming a new person, of new equipment, a new man. And here we are again in the middle of the statement of the problem and at the same time at the solution of both phenomena: rehabilitation and medicine of the person. There have always been severely injured people, but their number is increasing steadily today to a frightful degree. "Why me?" the afflicted person asks. He must learn to meet boldly the meaning of his disability and the new meaning of his life. The teacher J. G., a woman without hands, is a master of all everyday manual tasks and beyond that also of all feminine "manual" work. She knows that she provides better care for the students entrusted to her in the retraining school for new vocational skills than any non-handicapped colleague provides. Again and again new spiritual weapons against the fury of war spring to the mind of author M., Jur. D., blinded in the war. Such a listing could go on and on; the brief list of cases in the third section of this exposition may illustrate everything more clearly. It is not a matter of flight or of sinking into insensibility, nor a matter of resignation; it is a matter of the one, all-embracing answer. The Bible speaks about prayer for a pure heart and a new spirit. In medicine of the person as in total rehabilitation, the important thing is this one, simple, quiet truth: many common denominators, more than one common multiple.

What is rehabilitation? The literal translation of the foreign word—recovery of health—cannot satisfy, for it is not only a matter of a kind of mending, of overcoming the handicap, of becoming again a member of family life and work life, but of a "harmonious development of the personality, for which we want to make possible a life free from embitterment and inferiority complex." [5] Considered thus, rehabilitation is the "totality of all measures of a physical, psychological, pedagogical, or social kind," [6] and aspires to the greatest possible development of all the positive forces of the patient. A team of scientists, physicians, therapeutists is working toward that end. The eminent representative of German orthopedics, Biesalski, has already demanded the harmonious triad of hospital-school-workshop. But above and beyond that, there must exist for every handicapped person the possibility of gaining a new life meaning and life goal. Without such help from the doctor in the highest, most noble sense, all technical and economic work would be only piece work, only "loss of all real wisdom." [8] (Cases of semi- or pseudo-rehabilitation are sufficiently known; for reasons of space, negative results cannot be gone into here.) It is a matter therefore not only of the much-demanded economic security of the injured person. True rehabilitation is accomplished "by great desire for a new life . . . for overcoming of the externally inadequate, for a deliverance which wants more than momentary security." [9] It cannot be said more beautifully than with the words of one who went home much too soon: "The dignity of the handicapped fellow man requires in every case the attempt to still such desire tactfully, and with respect for the personal freedom of the handicapped person." [10]

In order to illustrate in total rehabilitation how great a question there is of personal encounter of human being to human being, personal commitment, mediation of the spiritual as integrating component of the person of the patient, and therefore of rehabilitation in the sense of a medicine of the person, a brief list of cases follows. (For reasons of space, medical history is limited to reference to the turning point, or the total rehabilitation which resulted despite permanence of the physical handicap.)

Case 1: Ingeborg de C., librarian; after acute poliomyelitis and meningitis, mobile on crutches, in a wheelchair, but also in a specially modified automobile; work at a desk. Harmonious, interested in art and science, anthroposophist.

Case 2: Irene Sch., previously office employee, since the end of the war almost completely paralyzed (likewise after polio);

painter; paints, draws, writes (shorthand also) with her mouth. Firmly grounded in religion (Roman Catholic). Great commitment of the mother. Internationally known as the illustrator and authoress of an English children's Bible (with illustrations in the style of the old masters).[11]

Case 3: Herbert F., Jur. D., high government official, blind and without hands as a result of the war; wounded as a young soldier, successfully completed his high-school and university studies with the help of a girl to read to him, started a family. Musical, intellectual, athletic, interested and creatively active in rehabilitation.

Case 4: X. K., M.D., also severely wounded as a young soldier, today active in a large pharmaceutical firm. During rehabilitation successful study, then professional practice, started a family. Not until recently did the last of his twenty-six facial operations take place (completion of the second side of the nose).

Case 5: A. Sch., M.D., neurologist; struck by acute poliomyelitis ten years ago in the middle of his work. The memory of his mother, who had once told him a deeply stirring story out of the life of Jesus, saved him from complete helplessness (paralysis of both arms and legs, artificial feeding, depths of depression). Here this rehabilitation began: the left hand learned to write; there followed attempts to move about in a wheelchair, resumption of rather light professional duties, concentration on a chiefly spiritual field of specialization. Aided by his courageous wife, Dr. Sch. carries on a large practice today, prescribing in a wheelchair. ". . . And it is precisely the physical handicap in everyday things which caused me to mature mentally in quiet hours." [12]

It does not need to be emphasized how full of blessings the work of a doctor, himself rehabilitated, can be. In this connection might also be mentioned the gigantic rehabilitation undertaking of Mlle. Suzanne Fouché in France. An extensive book could be written on this theme. In the previous pages much was only lightly touched or indicated; indeed, from lack of space many an important matter was not even mentioned. Also more was said of individual accomplishment than of the accomplishment of the doctor, the therapist, or the mother, who was often the deciding factor. All these people have their secret. Also many an exact report can give up only a part of it. "Everyone keeps his secret." [13] The rehabilitated handicapped person, the in fact no longer handicapped person (even though the respective physical handicap may persist) has perhaps—and this thought comes to me today not for the first time—a greater, deeper, more significant secret than so-called non-handicapped people. Does he not perhaps have at his disposal, for this very reason, special sources of power, at the same time sources of healing?

Notes

1. Paul Tournier, *Die Jahreszeiten unseres Lebens: Entfaltung und Erfüllung* [The Seasons of Our Life: Development and Fulfillment], vol. 76 of the Stundenbücher, new expanded edition of vol. 184 of the Furche-Bücherei, trans. Emilie Hoffman (Hamburg: Furche-Verlag, 1967), p. 91.
2. Ibid., p. 70.
3. Ibid., p. 69.
4. Ibid., p. 85.
5. W. Hagen, "Die Fürsorge für Körperbehinderte im Rahmen der Gesundheitsfürsorge" ["The Care of the Physically Handicapped in the Framework of Health Care"], in *Jahrbuch für Körperbehinderte* (Stuttgart: Thieme, 1956), pp. 31–35.
6. P. J. Briefs, "Rehabilitation," *Zeitschrift für Caritasarbeit und Caritaswissenschaft,* February 1956, p. 38.
7. K.-A. Jochheim, "Was ist Rehabilitation?" ["What Is Rehabilitation?"], in *Jahrbuch für Körperbehinderte* (Stuttgart: Thieme, 1962), pp. 14–19.
8. Paul Moor, *Gehorchen und Dienen* [Obeying and Serving] (Zürich: 1961).
9. Werner Dicke, "Der christliche Auftrag zur Rehabilitation Behinderter" ["The Christian Charge to Rehabilitation of the Handicapped"], in *Jahrbuch d. Deutschen Vereinigung f.d. Rehabilitation Behinderter* (Stuttgart: Thieme, 1965/66), pp. 43–46.
10. Ibid.
11. This case was publicized in many medical and other periodicals, e.g., I. Emich, "Ohnhänder schreiben und stenografieren" ["People without hands write and take shorthand"], Mat. Med. Nordmark, Uetersen 1962, XV, 5, pp. 182ff; I. Emich, "Totale Rehabilitation: eine Frage religiöser Bereitschaft" ["Total Rehabilitation: A question of religious preparedness"], *Soteria,* Utrecht 1966, X, 5, pp. 75ff.
12. From a letter of August 28, 1970. (The communication of this rehabilitation in the spirit of a medicine of the person I owe to the meeting in Hohenheim, 1970.)
13. Paul Tournier, *Jeder hütet sein Geheimnis* [Everyone has his secret] (Zürich/Stuttgart: 1965).

SUZANNE FOUCHÉ

Secretary General of L'ADAPT (League of
Organizations for Readaptation) and
Specialist in Reeducation and Readaptation
of Retarded and Inhibited Children
Paris, France

Reeducation and Medicine of the Whole Person

It was in 1943, in a barracks in Savoie, that I met Paul for the first time. We had been invited, both of us, to speak before a work yard of youth from the mountains—he, to tell about the whole person, and I, to incite these young chiefs to acquire a social formation. He had just published *Medicine of the Whole Person* and I, *Social Cases, Human Problems,* at the same time as a little social manual for youth from the work yards.

It was just before this whole group turned to the resistance movement, and we felt ourselves menaced by the surroundings. The notion of liberty of the whole person thus assumed a particular value.

Between us this was the total bond. What Paul said that evening about the unhurried attention he gave to his patients matched what I myself tried to do for the girls of the School of Baumes (Valence) which I directed. The great inspiration I received from him has been brightening my path ever since.

Personal experience had already taught me that a sick person does not suffer just in his body. Physical suffering totally invades the area of consciousness only if it is unbearable. But it does occupy it to some extent according to each individual's degree of tolerance. It recurs throughout the entire lifetime, and certainly the individual is affected by it through all the denials that it calls for.

Sickness or infirmity clouds primary needs: when one is not

hungry, when one sleeps poorly, when one is condemned to immobility, one is in a state of general uneasiness which places the very
joy of living in question. The doctor who prescribes severe regi-
mens and rigorous treatments should try to provide what com-
pensations he can. The very fact that he worries about what his
patient likes to eat, the manner in which he is placed in his bed
(even the weight of the covers on his feet), and what the imposed
immobility still permits him to do (a mirror and tweezers are
really useful), can be a great source of comfort. This kind of
personal attention soothes the patient who feels himself impris-
oned in his misery and sustains him in the effort to obey his
doctor's orders.

Wherever there is a question of an illness of long duration and
the state of the patient permits it, it is up to the doctor to suggest
all the proper measures to avoid confinement and withdrawal
from all social life. He must ask that the patient eat his meals at
the family table and prescribe a wheel chair or crutches for him
so that he can; he must authorize friendly visits and personal
work because the boredom which gnaws at the unoccupied patient
is more harmful than healthy fatigue from study or reading.

How many bedridden young people have wasted their lives
because the doctor forbade them all intellectual effort while their
long hours of solitude would have allowed them the exercise of
thought that could lead to the wonder of new discoveries? One
rapidly loses the working habit and takes a liking instead for the
passiveness of television viewing or easy reading. Then one day,
unprepared, one finds oneself before a closed future.

Sickness has the immense advantage of freeing us from engross-
ing routines. It creates available time. Out of respect to the
patient, the medical service of a hospital—doctor and nurses—
should keep to a regularity of schedule that would encourage him
in his personal planning. When he must wait an entire morning
for his doctor's visit or to have a dressing changed, he is incapable
of the concentration and self-denial that fertile thought demands.

From the moment of reorientation, it is really up to the chief of
the medical staff to provide guidance. He can help the patient
avoid the need for reorientation by recognizing his vocation as an
invaluable capital of knowledge, reflexes, attachment. Psychic
fatigue is less difficult to avoid than to relinquish. The doctor can
greatly encourage the patient to engage in his habitual activity by

sustaining him with something fortifying, but also and above all in hearing his admissions of weariness as many times as necessary until the system has triumphed.

If the patient's vocation is no longer suitable—and not only to the body but to the mind, to his ambition—it is time to change it. A bad orientation may perhaps have been one of the causes of the patient's illness.

It is not then exclusively for medical reasons that the doctor will advise a change of direction. As he considers the aspirations of that man, he will see that illness has perhaps caused him to question his previous activity and to desire the possibility of investing in his profession values that "retirement" has made him appreciate.

The doctor who has been in close contact with his patient during long months of illness knows how his patience has been called upon day after day, how his egocentricity from the beginning could be transposed into other interests; how unexpected and subtle insights have enriched his heart and his soul. He needs but one word to reveal to his patient that he has guessed this obscure progress toward a creative inner life, independent of models, which can no longer be set aside. May these dearly acquired values guide the patient's return to life and may all rancor against the testing he has undergone make room for the arrival of the mystery of providential ways.

The doctor who is a doctor of the whole person will help his patient to reorganize his way of life so as to preserve his healing, but without worrying him with exaggerated precautions and pro- hibitions. With him he will look for the joy his profession can bring to him, because for the handicapped, limited by abilities, the vocation must be the principal agent of his human flowering, and his professional successes must compensate for his curtailed social relationships.

The choice of leisure activities has, however, a fundamental importance. Well-considered advice will make the most of the possibilities. Participation in all sports is far from being system- atically ruled out; swimming, for example, provides relaxation and a satisfaction of the taste for spectacular risks. Riding, where man learns the limit of his power; the theater, ordinarily so little frequented; clubs which encourage friendly encounters—any- thing that can enchant the patient will assure a human balance favorable to the maintenance of his health.

Anxiously consulted with regard to marriage, the doctor will assume then one of his most serious responsibilities: is it good that this life be transmitted? Is one ever sure of his heredity? . . . But can one stop love from being born in a heart? And the home —is it not for man the ideal setting for protection as much as for enjoyment?

Thus, the doctor has contact with the person on every plane and the patient would like to be able to count on his advice. And it is not so much time for this that he complains of missing but the sympathy, the passion for man, and the love that must be the basis of the doctor's vocation.

What Paul Tournier has taught us is that one person cannot understand another if he does not accept being understood by him, that every gift of oneself demands mutual knowledge and confidence.

Paul Tournier has given his peers the example of the casting off of the dignity which stifles spontaneity. He has dropped the mask of indifference which hides emotions. He has given witness of a profound faith which transfigures his face and his word.

We have not dared to beg the doctor to come close to us. We have allowed him to be entrusted with our miseries; with our eyes closed we have accepted his prescriptions without confronting them with our obligations, without our being able to discuss them man to man in order to understand and accept them.

The doctor of the whole person is no longer the impassive Olympian about whom one can know nothing and whom we believe must be imposing to be effective. He knows that it is the whole man that he must demand of his patient and that he can only obtain this combination of forces by making himself a very active ally.

Then the patient, seeing the esteem in which he is held, begins to appreciate his own value, to discover the true dimensions of his personality. He accepts being himself and returning to life, without rancor for his suffering, without anxieties which leave him awkward. Rich from an experience whose rewards reassure those who fear it and solidly supported by the affirmation given to him by a man, he should be able to give to others of what he himself has received so much.

The doctor of the whole person as Paul Tournier wants it is a brother among his brothers. He is one of the cornerstones of the kingdom of heaven and earth.

FRANCESCO RACANELLI, M.D.

*Psychotherapist and Specialist
in Bioradiant Medicine
Florence, Italy*

Medicine of the Whole Person and Bioradiant Therapy

It is difficult to define something by denoting its limits and clearly determining through words its essential qualities. It is still harder to define man, "this unknown, taken from the earth and made in the image and likeness of God."

If this man, from a state of normal health, falls into a pathological state, it becomes difficult to understand him in his totality as a sick man, since he must be understood to be healed. To heal a man is not simply to free him from a physical malady but also from psychic suffering.

The action of healing requires a technique taught in medical school, which acts on the patient as *res*, a thing, an organism "taken from the earth." But for man, made "in the image and likeness of God," what is it that acts to heal him? Certainly not the surveying technique learned at school, but the art of the doctor as a man who takes the acquired technique and adapts it to each patient.

To care for a patient in order to heal him implies a technical rapport of the doctor to the patient, and a human rapport, a contact between the doctor as man and the sick man. Consequently, if "poeta nascitur, medicus nascitur et fit." One becomes a doctor if one has a natural calling which has as its foundation the acceptance of the other person, the sick man, and respect for his dignity as a human being. This is only possible by grace of an emotional responsibility which permits taking another person to heart, of understanding him: "cum prehendere." This art is taught only by life, in daily work, insofar as the individual is involved to the total ability of his humanity.

The healing vocation becomes more conscious from day to day along the professional path of each doctor. A vocation which is perhaps stifled by exterior contingencies: the necessity for a higher gain which makes of the profession a business which has become a succession of technical actions; the difficulties of a socialized medicine which takes up a lot of time filling out administrative forms; the obligation to hurry because of the large number of patients who are tired of the prolonged wait in the consultation room, and so forth.

In spite of the various external difficulties, the true vocation is nurtured by the flame of compassion and love toward the sufferer. The doctor as a man cannot remain isolated in this long struggle against internal and external difficulties, but he needs the comfort and support of his associates who are striving to attain the same goal, the healing of sick men.

In August of 1948, as a good Catholic practicing according to the norms of the future Vatican II Council, I made a retreat at the convent of the Sisters of Grandchamp, near Neuchâtel. I participated in the religious activity, following the ritual of prayers and songs in the chapel, and I helped take care of the garden. This facilitated conversations and deep dialogues with the sisters. One day Sister Marguerite of Beaumont, the mother prioress, said to me: "You ought to meet Doctor Paul Tournier of Geneva; he would do you a lot of good. Besides, you have something in common. Not a lot," she added, smiling. "Tell him that you are coming because of me."

I arrived in Geneva at Champel Street, where Dr. Tournier then lived. He and Nelly received me with affectionate courtesy, inviting me to dinner. This was a feast for body and soul.

Thus I encountered medicine of the whole person. From that moment, I have participated in almost every one of the "weeks of medicine of the whole person."

Among the passionate and tenacious founders of the Bossey weeks, as well as among colleagues belonging to different nationalities, religions, and the most diversified temperaments, who have come to increase and rejuvenate the movement, I have found the support necessary to pursue the path traced by my

medical vocation. From each participation at the week of study
and meditation of the medicine of the whole person I have returned to my work culturally enriched through the teachings of
the conferences and the biblical studies exposed by Dr. Tournier
with the fascinating sympathy which emanates from a man rich
with culture and humanity, who believes in what he says and
professes. I was at the same time psychologically comforted by
personal encounters in which a reciprocal exchange of life experiences took place.

Medicine of the whole person, bioradiant therapy: is there a
difference? And in what does it consist?

One cannot practice bioradiant medicine without practicing
medicine of the whole person, in the same manner as the latter
requires knowledge of psychosomatic and organic medicine.

Bioradiant therapy is the medicine of the whole person insofar
as the doctor who professes it resolves his own problems as a
doctor as a person, over against those of himself and his family in
his social, professional, economic, and political relationships. Since
man gives what he has in order to pronounce words and to
accomplish important acts in life, that is to say, rituals, the doctor
must have realized and harmonized in himself what he wants
and should give to his patient as a human creature.

Man's difficulties are particularly his; having resolved and risen
above them, it will be easy for him to go beyond the external
difficulties that procure things and men for him. In like manner,
he conquers an availability and a liberty which are conscious and
rational responsibilities.

The doctor can attain this interior level only if he considers
himself as a patient to care for daily, objectively, and with the
necessary therapeutic austerity which can impose psychic operations on himself. He must accept and transcend everything within
and outside himself to enrich his therapeutic power—therapeutic
power made up of scientific knowledge, of fully lived and past
experiences in contact with Life.

Life is God, and Jesus Christ is the soul manifested from this
Life, in its multiple forms: the cosmic Christ. Consequently, the
other and I, all other living beings and I, things and I, are one,
well established in a hierarchy of essential values by which man
is the king of nature. In fact, man is, among terrestrial beings, the

most responsible, the most creative, son of Mother Earth, but above all, son of God, the Spirit, creator of the visible and invisible world.

This imposes on man a discipline, spiritual exercise which frees him from the weight of his *id*, his individual nature as the center of the world. In order to arrive at the summit of the mountain of life, where the individual places his reliance on another to help him realize the fullness of his successful talents, man must know how to die himself in order to find himself as liberated love in the next one he encounters.

In this way, the doctor becomes everything to his patient—a bridge, leavening. And if the patient is completely healed—that is to say, healed in body and enriched in soul, thanks to the experience of his sickness—the element of transition goes even further. In this case, the doctor, already part of past experience, now becomes a living remembrance, a beneficial image; and the man, already healed, walks along to encounter other experiences.

Each sickness has a finality for each patient, a goal, a reality to incarnate. A doctor of the whole person helps his patient to realize it. The patient "passes over" the doctor as he might over a bridge in order to find the goal that the experience of his sickness may show him.

There are some patients for whom the doctor must operate therapeutically in their existence like leaven, that is, like the presence of a vitalizing ferment, or catalyst. Leaven in all substances is an energy of life which stimulates biological transformation. In like manner, the action of the doctor affects his patient as a person; in fact, he is a presence, neither possessive nor deforming, but freely offered and liberating.

In order to attain this therapeutic action in which the doctor, as a person, becomes medicine, the latter must be evolved to the point of love united with knowledge. Love-knowledge imposes upon the person who desires to incarnate it in order to live it, a continual transcendence of the humanity of his id, *subject*, in order to become *object* to himself, a living and purifying agent. Then the man, as an individual, does not appraise the actions and reactions of others in relation to himself, since, in order to realize the just relationships in his life as a man and doctor, he does not count. In fact, he appraises the other, his patient, in his human condition, and responds to him through thought, words, and positive, comforting and therapeutic acts. In order to do that, he is not moved by sentiment, but by the love-knowledge through which he gives to the other only what he can assimilate and consequently is due him.

The therapeutic response of such a doctor is not emotional, but rational and spiritual. His practice follows the ethic of life: so that the latter may be manifested in order to realize the fullness of the other, the sick man, considered objectively as a son of God, but conditioned by successful talents.

For this rapport in life, the doctor-man must necessarily become a religious creature; that is, he must be united with his neighbor and with the Divinity. This religiousness, lived daily, leads man to live with others, in others. In order to be able to become leaven—personal presence, not an individual for whom dialogue is *I-you*, but impersonal person, *I in you*—one must arrive at solitude, this solitude through which man honors God in his love for another. This love strengthens him in humility because he records in his work an insufficient amount of it every day. He accepts the weakness of the human creature, exalted in his faith in Jesus Christ, in his surrender to God the Creator of visible and invisible life.

Tied to this consciously accepted set of spiritual exercises, the doctor of the whole person practices bioradiant medicine.

PAUL PLATTNER, M.D.

Psychiatrist and
Director of Mental Hospital
Münchenbuchsee, Switzerland

The Person of the Doctor in Medicine of the Whole Person

The person is complex and unitary, completed and constantly changing. Person is detached from the environment and yet intimately connected to it, autonomous and yet challenged. One can speak of person only in paradoxes. This holds true as much for the person of the patient as for the person of the doctor, a matter which is to be the chief subject of this article.

How did Paul Tournier become that person who is to be honored by this publication? Not only has he practiced *médecine de la personne* professionally in an especially impressive and exemplary way, but he has set and continues to set an example to us all again and again with his whole being. It is precisely in this unity of profession and personal life that a first characteristic and essential personality trait for the doctor of the medicine of the person becomes visible.

In an essay from the year 1950,[1] Paul Tournier describes his personal development himself. After an apologia for scientific accuracy, which follows from, among other things, the "incomparable precision" of modern laboratory and research methods, and which seems to provide the doctor in diagnostics and therapy a certainty never before known, Tournier, in his exposition, suddenly makes a surprising leap into a complete unknown. The patient is no longer seen, described, examined, and treated by him only as object, but he retains the dignity of a self-responsible subject with a voice in making decisions. In the course of the final

manner of consideration, which completes the purely casual diagnosis to that point, Tournier speaks abruptly of a second, a
spiritual-final-subjective diagnosis, which not the doctor, but only
the patient himself can produce, "for only he himself perceives
the ultimate end, what God wants to say to him through the
occurrence of the illness." We can, however, be helpful to our
patients in reaching the diagnosis, in the degree to which we
ourselves also listen to the voice of God in our lives. Then we can
also do this in communion with the patients and benefit both their
spiritual life and ours by the communion.

In the readiness and courage for such a transcending of all
official and scholastic boundaries—here in full recognition of the
person of the patient, and in striving for an essentially deepened
spiritual communion, clearly beyond the usual therapeutic contact—I see a second feature which should characterize the doctor
of medicine of the person. With Paul Tournier this readiness is
not only the pouring out of his rich and many-faceted nature, but
also a consequence of his spiritual experience.

After praise of scientific medicine, we read in Tournier's essay
that, with "many whom the doctor could help," the help is offered
less through "what we prescribe or advise than through a mysterious personal influence, which science by no means can explain." He describes then how, through "a series of personal
spiritual experiences, not only his personal and married life was
illuminated, clarified, and enriched by God, but also his whole
professional activity received a new meaning."

These personal changes, with Paul Tournier and with many
who can experience them, led to the experience that patients,
"without in the slightest being urged to do so, suddenly give up
hitherto anxiously guarded secrets," and that between them and
the doctor a human communion develops which both have sought
in vain up to that point.

This communion, already discussed above, is a third distin-
guishing mark of that special doctor-patient relationship which
the medicine of the person strives for. A condition for giving it to
both partners, doctor and patient—for it cannot be at all arbitrarily produced or forced—obviously consists in a preparatory
spiritual liberation of the doctor. Experience shows again and
again that a doctor who is really intrinsically free from prejudice
—who, unbiased, meets his patients as fellow creatures—helps

them to their own inner freedom. It is as if a freeing inner experience were contagious. This inner freedom can be considered a further characteristic which one might wish for the doctor of medicine of the person.

We find out how the activation of the patient can take place through contact with the doctor in Alphons Maeder, one of the fathers of medicine of the person. In one of his books he describes his personal development from the purely scientific-causal oriented pupil of Freud to a psychotherapist with a final-prospective basic attitude, and therefore an attitude obligated to the spirit.

Maeder's works revolve again and again around the theme of the doctor/patient relationship. He gradually discovered in it something much more deeply imprinted from the spirit than corresponds to the orthodox-analytical theory of transference. The development of this recognition can be gathered, in key-phrases as it were, from the titles of his publications. In our connection this is illuminating for the reason that the significance of the person of the doctor is increasingly more clearly stressed, and at the same time the connection with the classical conception of the doctor/patient relationship still remains discernible.

Maeder's first work in this series still carried the title: "The Doctor as Psychotherapeutic Factor." [2] In the following work there is already mention of a "psychotherapeutic agent." [3] The doctor becomes nothing more than something neutral, understood as a "factor," but still not as a personal being. This decisive step Maeder makes with the book: *The Psychotherapist as Partner*.[4] Maeder's last work in this series, to a certain degree his spiritual testament, really ought to carry the title, as he wrote to me personally: *The Apellatus* (The one called).[5] As "one called," Maeder designates in his book the doctor as well as the patient. More exactly stated, it is a matter of the person of the doctor and the person of the patient, and, to be sure, under the aspect that both are addressed in common by a spiritual something, a third one, hovering over them, summoned by God.

With the help of the partnership between doctor and patient, and in the security which is given to both by the spiritual, the patient can loosen his dependence on the world, on his symptoms, on his sickness and his suffering. The powers of affirmation and regeneration slumbering in the patient, the mental self-direction, which is by no means identical with the understanding or the conscious will, can be activated in this "heart-to-heart encounter, this meeting of human being with human being, of center with center." For such a development to open up, however, the words of Martin Buber hold true in this partnership: "Whoever wants to talk with a person, without talking to God, his words do not come to fruition; but whoever wants to talk to God without talking to people, his words go astray." [6]

In the first part of Buber's essay the doctor is warned against his narcissism. This forms, especially for the doctor who is admired or even "worshipped" by the patient, a lasting danger. The active therapy of the committed, helpful doctor, be he surgeon, obstetrician, psychotherapist or general practitioner, demands a lasting, watchful self-control. Gebsattel speaks in this connection of a "humility lived." That is also saying that the doctor be conscious that he himself does not set the values. Together with the patient, he is obligated to superpersonal spiritual forces, to that third one encountered by everyone who wants to act in real responsibility, and who does not want to succumb to the temptation of Lucifer. In this I see a further demand upon the person of the doctor in medicine of the person.

The second part of Martin Buber's admonition—that one should not want to talk to God without talking to human beings—points us toward love of our fellow-man, to the genuine brotherly unity with the suffering ones entrusted to us. The important thing is that the love which we know is a source of knowledge as well as of power.

The knowledge which springs from this love completes the insights gained by the scientific-objective method. Frequently it alone can give these methods the proper orientation in a consideration which includes, in diagnosis and plan of treatment, not only the individual organs of the sick person, but also the totality of his actual personal situation as a fellow human being in all its aspects. It goes without saying that the ability to speak with each person in language appropriate to that person is a part of this brotherly love. The doctor of the person does not obstruct access to him through a purposeless and thoughtless discussion about God; he does not want to convert but to understand, not to preach but to listen and to share. Out of this love grows the power to stand by the patient with help and healing, even when the doctor's efforts are rewarded with no success in the usual medical sense. The medical-humane assistance must stand the test of incurable suffering or a resistant-reluctant patient. In this I see the trial by fire to which each doctor must set himself, and more than ever, of course, the doctor who would like to practice his profession under the sign of *médecine de la personne.*

Notes

1. "Die neue Sendung des Arztes" ["The New Mission of the Doctor"], in *Sammlung Jurisprudenz-Medizin-Philosophie-Theologie,* Part 13/14, ed. Prof. Dr. H. Urban (Innsbruck: Tyrolia Verlag, 1950).
2. Alphons Maeder, "The Significance of the Doctor as a Psychotherapeutic Factor," lecture in the SGP, 1923.
3. A. Maeder, "The Person of the Doctor, a Psychotherapeutic Agent," from a lecture in the French language.
4. A. Maeder, *Der Psychotherapeut als Partner* [The Psychotherapist as Partner] (Zürich: 1957); *Studien zur Kurztherapie* [Studies in Short-Term Therapy] (Stuttgart: 1963); *Sendung und Aufgabe des Arztes* [Mission and Task of the Doctor] (Zürich: 1952).
5. For publisher's reasons, however, it came out under the title *Studien zur Kurztherapie* [Studies in Short-Term Therapy].
6. Martin Buber, *Ich und Du* [I and Thou] (Heidelberg: 1958) *Zwiesprache* [Dialog] (Berlin: 1932).

ANDRÉ SARRADON, M.D.

Specialist in Psychosomatic Medicine
Marseille, France

This Unceasing Quest

Evocation, by subjective notes, of the experience of the progressive medical transition of a practitioner; up to and including the discovery of the medicine of the whole person.

Who, therefore, has not followed this route?

Choice of studies, of profession: scientific curiosity (what a beautiful mechanism, man . . .); psychological flavor (what a luxurious zoological garden, humanity . . .); by his side "the Saint Bernard dog" (to brighten up in the exchange!); the example lived by a father, a friend, in his role of physician (the image, the model . . .); the project takes form, the identification begins . . . and underneath, so many things ignored, found only long afterwards.

Here I am, "sawbones": fundamental sciences, the hospital, the operating team, to be a surgeon!

Then the finesse of a diagnostician, the qualities of judgment, the human approach, the being in his environment, so many things to know, to discover by contact with reality . . . I will be a physician.

After the disappointment of religions, of philosophies, the rapture of finding a new virginity of thought, an expectation . . .

Anguish and joy of installation, of practice: this infant, this body without thought, what a pure medical object! He does not eat: parcel of Bourget, vitamins. Then one day, a small dull being, a pale look, without a cry, beside a snarly, curt mother;

this woman suffering in the stomach: nothing organic, infectious, hormonal; then the husband returns from work; the atmosphere of the house suddenly weighs down heavily . . . but everything clears up.

And then follow the sick, asking for service, like at the mechanic's (unclog my carburetor, change my tire). Yes, but these symptoms which they display; this request, often hidden under denials; this appeal, what is it? Take me in your charge, help me to live.

I do not recognize any more my beautiful sick of the hospital, with specimens of anatomical pathology, their germs identified . . . only rarely.

And all the others?

Psychofunctional troubles, psychic illnesses, psychosomatic states . . . the waltz of labels, the prefabricated drawers of nosology, the names in a catch-all file, which hide what? which hide whom?

This morbid entity, isolated as if in a test tube, this one who "has" this illness, that he has "caught"? Or this sick man who expresses his suffering, his disappointment, the drama of his relation to others . . .

At what does one play? To classify, to arrange: diagnostics on the one hand, therapeutic remedy on the other; one juxtaposes, one knows, one acts.

But one day, like a weariness, an unsatisfaction . . .

One leafs through references, one studies books, one works hard. To understand at last? So much knowledge accumulated, so much ignorance of which to fill the gap; and the strange feeling arises: the library of the world will no longer suffice . . .

Then, a need: to meet men, the men who are searching also, questioning unceasingly their experience in life, their acquaintance with life.

Mystery of knowing.

Whence the first contact with Bossey: a brotherhood united in its discovery of the Whole Person, which urges it, which does not succeed in defining it, which does not look for any more words for it; a comprehension so much more precise than signs, communication on this side of speech.

Authenticity of oneself, with the others.

Medicine of the whole person, a haven at first; but from whence one takes to the road again—another road . . .

ARMAND VINCENT, M.D.

General Practitioner and
Specialist in Preventive Medicine
Paris, France

From Fireside Medicine to Team Medicine of the Whole Person

Each man is a story which is identical to no other.

—Alexis Carrel

Paul Tournier has told us many times how he proceeded when at the beginning of his career he demonstrated the effect on patients' health of their attitude before God and before their own problems. He invited them to come speak about their life "in the evening by the fireside," and he did not make them pay because "this wasn't medicine any more." We are not surprised that the body of medical practice is still resisting medicine of the whole person, since Paul Tournier, himself, only forty years ago, thought this was "not medicine."

When Paul Tournier realized the importance for his patients' health of their attitude about life, he no longer hesitated to listen to them talk about it in his consulting room. This was indeed the work of the doctor. Already "fireside medicine" loomed. The essential still remained: the doctor-patient contact, the necessity of a humane medicine, meeting the person in his totality and looking for his place in the cosmos, in God's plan.

Thus, Paul Tournier, consecrating his time, his patience, and his love to his patients, learned to listen to them talk about their often overlapping personal, social, and spiritual problems. Without breaking the relationship, he had them go into his "white room," where their body is exposed to medical technique without

196

By the fireside
1969

their person escaping from the doctor's action. Their attitude toward sickness and toward life is often pinpointed even in the course of a somatic examination.

Medicine of the whole person was born of a doctor who succeeded, through personal effort, in taking heed of his passion for human contact and also of his own attitudes toward the patient, sickness, and God. Paul Tournier has proved to us the therapeutic value of communication. He has revealed to us the existence, conjoined with technical medicine, of a relative medicine. He has lifted for us the veil which used to mask the hidden face of medicine.

The doctor of the whole person must be one because *the unity of the person* is manifested to him under three indivisible aspects through which he can approach it:

—The human body is part of the person.

—The psyche makes the person aware of himself.

—The mind is the nucleus of the person.

If a single aspect is manifested, the others are underlying and always present. It is classic to have access from the psychic to the spiritual. It is popular to pass from the somatic to the psychic and vice versa. It is possible to go from the somatic to the spiritual.

Every person is different from every other person, as much in his total make-up as in each of his aspects. That is why medicine of the whole person is difficult and cannot be resolved in equations. But harmony of the three aspects is necessary to the equilibrium of the person, since it is not so much a question of prolonging the duration of life as of making happiness possible, and open a door to spiritual essence.

The doctor of the whole person must know somatic medicine and never forget it. Without being a psychoanalyst, he must be abreast of psychic mechanisms, somewhat clarified by Freud, Jung, Adler and their students. He must know psychosomatic medicine, and the Balint method of formation could help him there. He must take note that all his words, his silences, his acts, his attitudes count, and those of the patient equally. The handling of the doctor-patient relationship is extremely difficult, and the doctor of the whole person will learn it through practice, though even at the end of his career he will still be making mistakes.

The enormous difficulty for a doctor of the whole person is to maintain the equilibrium of the three aspects, without which there is no longer a whole person. Two dangers threaten him: He risks shutting himself up in spirituality and taking pleasure in it, moving towards theology and philosophy and then no longer being a doctor. The other danger comes from outside, from the public. As the doctor of the whole person listens to people talk and sometimes as he talks, they make a psychotherapist of him, which he is not. Paul Tournier himself could not escape the second danger, even though he defended himself against it all his life and sometimes even fled to the first danger.

There is, fortunately, a straight way that can save the doctor of the whole person if he will engage in it. It is the difficult problem of patients without problems. They do not go to the psychotherapist and no one sends them to the psychiatrist. Somatic doctors help them only in a transitory way. Finally they end up at the doctor of the whole person's who listens to them. But they have nothing to say.

"There are problems in every life. There are dramas in every heart," says Paul Tournier. That is true. But, perhaps happily, few men are conscious of it. Or the problem will seem to them to be such a little thing, shoved so far back in their consciousness that it does not occur to them to talk about it, still less to consult a psychiatrist. Then they meet a doctor who loves them and whom they love, who knows how to listen to their inability to express themselves, to prescribe good medicine for them, on which they fix their transference, which is a vehicle of medicine of the whole person. It is a doctor who does not look very scholarly, whose prescription pad does not list too many titles, whose car is not too powerful. But he listens to them, he smiles to them, and he loves them. Then, one day, at the end of the consultation, the patient without a problem brings out his problem. Oh, such a very little problem! a little self-conscious, very lame: the little girl who passes in front of the house without coming in to say good day, the son-in-law who is so busy that he does not have the time to come over, the grandson who cannot be made to make "his communion," even though he is of age, the beautiful girl who fails all her exams, the butcher who looks down on you, while the grocer even gives you little extras; the cat who makes messes on the carpet or doesn't come home. These are some of the little problems which hide bigger ones, and the big one will come out the next time. But by then the medicine-vehicle will have had its little effect. "Fireside medicine" has become medicine of the medical office.

Science and technique are also gifts of God. That they are often marred through human errors does not remove them from consideration.

Scientific, technical and spiritual progress have at the same time complicated somatology, psychology, sociology, and theology. Each one of these sciences can no longer be the domain of a single man. Their knowledge, their practice, and their advancement involve specialization.

Indispensable specialization pushes analysis a very long way, and breaks man and his social relationships into very small pieces. It goes counter to the unity of the person desired by God.

The specialist can remain a doctor of the whole person, however. It depends upon his attitude toward the patient and his own conscience for "fireside medicine" to give its tonality to medicine of the specialist.

Man is a social being. The human person does not exist individually. He is the component of a community. Community itself is a person of persons, unifying spiritual exigencies both of the individual and the community.

Caring for a person can only be done while caring for other persons. Caring for a child necessitates treating his parents, his fellow-playmates, co-workers and the people in his neighborhood. It is only at this price that medicine of the whole person will be preventive. "It is right to watch over the patient to cure him, his health to conserve it," says Hippocrates in his *Treatise of Precepts*.

Preventive medicine is at one and the same time individual and social. It demands the sanitary education of the community. Moreover, there is no good curative medicine without a spirit of prevention at its base. To care for a diabetic is not to treat gangrene or a coma, it is to prevent such accidents.

Man's health is influenced by the way he eats, dresses, houses himself, dies, works, amuses himself, worships God, thinks— in a word, the way in which he lives. Nothing of all this is of no matter to the doctor of the whole person who is integrated into the community.

But today the individual doctor feels overwhelmed by the

volume of knowledge, by the parceling out of medical tasks, by the demanding attitude justly claimed by the consumers, by social evolution, by financial cast of medicine that necessitates the intervention of collectivism.

Such is the problem of our time.

The solution in the medical domain implies at one and the same time a change in men and a change in structures. To change the latter does not suffice to change man, but to change man can make these structures adaptable to his condition.

Let us hope that the doctor may change and become a doctor of the whole person. In his individual medical practice he is not taking the way concurrent to ours. If he would like to change, he could not, so implacable is the socio-economic shell that clings to him. The doctor's turning in upon his little self, his little environment, the lack of exchanges, the locking out of the great currents which are turning the world upside down, do not favor his clairvoyance and his action at all. He must open himself up to scientific progress, to the currents of contemporary thought, and follow the social evolution and the march of humanity.

Let us hope that the inevitable change of structures may be accomplished in a sense favorable to the development of medicine of the whole person; that is to say, toward medicine in an organized team.

The nursing team, composed of a surgeon, his aides, his auxiliary personnel, or of a specialist and his technicians, or still, of a chief of service, his assistants, his auxiliaries, is a type of pyramidal team. It implies at its summit a moving spirit. If that individual is open to the person, the team will quickly use medicine of the whole person. This type of team has already been functioning for several years in certain services for the chronically ill: mental, bronchial, or tubercular patients, renal patients using an artificial kidney, physically or mentally handicapped patients. Modern treatment of these ailments necessitates collaboration of personnel with various skills: doctors, professional masseurs, psychotherapists, ergotherapists, nurses, instructors, educators. If one of them has a privileged contact with the patient, it is through him that the team can conduct its action.

"Fireside medicine" has already penetrated into institutional medicine.

The homogenous medical team, uniting similar elements, is a spherical type. It is constituted of doctors of the same discipline, most often general practitioners, who take charge simultaneously of the health of the population in a particular sector, on educative, preventive, and curative planes. It is necessary that all team doctors, even though sometimes different in their techniques, have in common a respect for the human being.

The work of sanitary education and prevention, which is not being done at the present time (or very little of it is being done) will place the medical team in contact with the population in advance of all curative acts. Between the two of them a human relationship will be established, the prelude to an eventual doctor-patient relationship. In case of sickness, the free choice of the doctor can be made truly conscientiously. This choice having been made, and well made, the patient will always be attended by his own personal doctor. In the latter's absences or in a case of emergency, he will not be treated like an unknown but rather by one of the other team doctors whom he knows and who has access to his medical record. The members of this team, moved by the same spirit and trained through their daily contact to life in dialogue, will be more available to the patients who have chosen them and more likely to look among themselves and their associates for the appropriate solution in each case.

The doctor-patient relationship can be carried out in three forms, each of which includes love of one's fellow-man:

—"Transference," pivot of psychoanalysis, is possible in every long and regular therapeutic relationship.

—"Sympathy" is more popular.

—"Empathy" is the most favorable form of the relationship. The doctor understands the situation of the other through a process of identification, but at the same time keeps a certain distance, permitting himself to remain an observer and to keep a cool head.

That the patient may have an empathetic relationship with his personal doctor and a sympathetic relationship with the other members of the team is certainly the most favorable situation, and the one toward which the team should strive.

The team will strive in each case to attain the equilibrium of the person which will make possible the quest for happiness. But there are some patients who stubbornly hang on to their neuroses and, rather than being cured, prefer to continue suffering. Psychoanalysts and psychosomaticians abandon them as an inevitable loss. Medicine of the whole person practiced in a team, with its communal resources, will be better fixed to understand their refusal, to follow them in their social life, eventually to extend an always available hand.

The manner in which the doctor treats a man can either help the latter to become more human or it can dehumanize him. The way in which the doctor serves society can render it more sociable or, on the contrary, abandon it to the totalitarian danger.

Medicine in an organized team, practiced by selected mature and trained doctors, reconciles the exigencies of the illness and the object-patient with those of the personalized subject. Through it, the doctor is placed between the human person and the community, in order to protect and serve both of them. Through it, fireside medicine, which has already found a place in the general practitioner's office and in the specialist's office, can benefit preventive medicine, everyday medicine, institutional medicine, and thus add new dimensions to the medicine of the whole person.

RAMON REY ARDID, M.D.

Professor, Psychiatrist
Zaragoza, Spain

Psychosomatic Medicine and the Medicine of the Whole Person

In 1947, Paul Tournier, Alphonse Maeder and Jean de Rougemont sent out the invitation to the first "Week at Bossey" which brought together thirty-two European physicians, most of whom were Swiss, French, German, Italian and Dutch. This was to be the core of the "Bossey group," founders of the medicine of the whole person, whose leader was and will always be Paul Tournier. At later meetings (Bossey, Oosterbeck, Weissenstein, Athens, Rüschlikon, Versailles, Bad Boll, Getsemani, etc.), which took place almost annually, the Bossey group grew with the addition of colleagues from Spain, Greece, the Scandinavian countries, Belgium, the Americas and other countries.

I have no intention of defining the medicine of the whole person, since I am writing these few lines of homage to Paul Tournier on the occasion of his seventy-fifth birthday and they are likely to be read mainly by doctors of the whole person. My only wish is to try to establish certain boundaries to the domain of the Bossey movement, that is, to define its essence, so badly understood by some. Let us begin by underlining an historic fact: the period during which the Bossey movement had its beginnings coincided with the great expansion of psychosomatic medicine (von Weizsäcker, D. Franders, etc.) in Europe and America. This coincidence, due to change or more likely to cultural factors, has without doubt been the reason that the medicine of the whole person has been too often considered, even by scientists, synonymous with psychosomatic medicine or at least as a branch of it. In many articles and at some of the Bossey meetings I have noticed this, above all among American and German colleagues.

It must be admitted that the ideas of psychosomatic medicine were a great step forward, one which expanded the horizons of medicine and enriched the techniques of therapy, because they permitted us to consider the patient as a suffering human being, subject not only to pain, worry, and bodily discomfort but also to the psychic consequences of all these. They taught us, at the same time, that there are several maladies (of which a few, like the duodenal ulcer, bronchial asthma, colitis, and myocardial infarction, show an interior lesion) which are largely due to emotional and psychic causes, and for which the treatment must be not only pharmaceutic and physiotherapeutic, even surgical, but also psychotherapeutic. Psychosomatics has doubled the physician's picture of his patient, since it added the psychological factor to pathology and therapy as an instrument for cure and prophylaxis. It would be hard now to imagine a doctor who would dare to discount the psychic side of his patients. The modern physician cannot remain a pure technician. He needs to be at the same time a psychologist and, frequently, a sociologist.

If we were to look for the origins of psychosomatics we would find them, doubtless, in the ideas which the "Freudian revolution" has brought us, after which the physician realized that he needed to get closer to his patient. True, there are other branches of psychosomatic medicine which dispense with psychoanalysis—in fact, do not accept it (for example those who are studying the neurophysiological or sociological factors of sickness)—but in any case one must recognize that the psychosomatic attitude of the modern physician stems from psychoanalysis and the psychodynamic concepts it brought to medical thought.

The old nature-scientific somaticist medicine of the nineteenth century has become psychosomatic medicine without losing the strictly scientific approach, adding new pathogenic concepts to our classic concepts concerning sickness, such as the new technique of psychotherapy has done for the usual somatic methods of treatment. But psychosomatic medicine does not embrace all the dimensions of the human being. It considers the sick person as a psychocorporal complex, the elements of which interact, often decisively, in the dynamics of sickness. But, in spite of all, the patient remains an *individual*—child, man or woman, belonging to the realm of animals, though richly endowed psychically. He is bound to the earth. Everything outside this earth, everything the patient feels as a *person*, with his transcendence, his beliefs, his life problems, his religious feelings, his guilt feelings, his fear of death, or his plans for a better life after he is cured—all this remains outside the field of action of the psychosomatic physician, who certainly works with psychic factors but at the same time neglects the spiritual factors.

Indeed, the reality of the sick person is that here is a human being, a person, who is undergoing not only the malady with its natural effects and consequences but also those which are reflected in the supernatural, transcendent and spiritual realms. This is why the psychosomatic practitioner cannot meet all the needs of the patient as a person, calm his fears, help clear up his life problems, alleviate his feeling of aloneness, counsel him concerning his doubts and hesitancies, and strengthen his faith, not only through his technical and professional techniques, but in his personal involvement with him and with the divinity. The doctor of the whole person, above all, is a man who believes in the supreme dignity of mankind and who sees in his patient a person who is experiencing a crisis, not only corporal but spiritual, and who feels himself strongly called to accomplish with him a mission, complete and total, as a doctor and as a human being. But this personal attitude, this spiritual communion between doctor and patient, is not possible without the religious spirit in the former. It is for this reason that the doctor of the whole person must be religious in the broadest and purest sense of the word. Indeed, to be capable of, to always be ready to come to the aid of the patient with spiritual problems, they have to be understood in an absolutely human manner, with real compassion.

While avowing that the medicine of the whole person requires *a priori* a religious attitude on the part of the physician, one must recognize that it is not specifically religious in the conventional sense of the word, though created by Christian doctors. I dare say there is no medicine, religious, pastoral or missionary, which only religious doctors could practice. I prefer to state that, above all, the medicine of the whole person is integral, complete, that it fulfills all the needs of the patient, somatic, psychological and spiritual. It is therefore an attitude, a "way of acting," and belongs to any doctor who is capable of "pouring" himself completely and without reserve into the spiritual situation of his patients.

These feelings are doubtless awakened or at least stimulated by the religious faith—no matter which, if it is alive and sincere—and it is for this reason that the doctor of the whole person always sees in his patient a fellow-creature in the real evangelical sense and also—why not?—other religions. And it is for this reason too that he wants to help this fellow-creature, not only in his sickness, as a turning of his life curve, but also in the personal crisis brought about by the sickness, like an obstacle on his biographical curve. In order to do this, the physician must first help himself, that is, when he meets his patient he must be tranquil in soul and cleansed in spirit. This condition, not necessary in somatic or psychotherapeutic technique, is indispensable in the medicine of the whole person, since it requires a veritable communion between the physician and his patient.